6.00

SURTSEY

SIGURDUR THORARINSSON

SURTSEY

THE NEW ISLAND IN THE NORTH ATLANTIC

Translated by Sölvi Eysteinsson

THE VIKING PRESS · NEW YORK

Layout: Torfi Jónsson

Photographic reproduction: Recato Offset A/S

Typesetting, printing of text, and binding:
Schultz Bogtrykkeri

Printing plates: Nordgrafik A/S

Copyright 1964 in all countries of the International
Copyright Union, © *1966 by Almenna Bókafélagið.*

Published in 1967 by
The Viking Press, Inc.
625 Madison Avenue, New York, N. Y. 10022

Distributed in Canada by
The Macmillan Company of Canada Limited

Library of Congress catalog card number 67–10220

Printed and bound in Copenhagen, Denmark.

A special wonder wrought by God

"At three o'clock in the morning we saw smoke rising from the sea and thought it to be land; but on closer consideration we concluded that this was a special wonder wrought by God and that a natural sea could burn."

This was a report written by Jörgen Mindelberg, captain of the brig *Boesand,* on his sailing to Iceland in the spring of 1783 when he and his crew were the first to witness a submarine eruption to the southwest of Reykjanes on the morning of May 1st. Having signed his report on this volcanic activity and the island which appeared as a result of it the captain added the following confession: "When I caught sight of this terrifying smoke I felt convinced that Doomsday had come"(i)*.

Volcanic fires at sea and the appearance of a new island may, indeed, be regarded as a remarkable wonder in nature, but such happenings are not unique, particularly off the coasts of Iceland.

Mid-Atlantic ridge on dry land

An explanation of the frequent volcanic eruptions in Iceland and off the Icelandic coasts is partly to be found in the geological situation of the country. Iceland has a central position among the landmasses which were piled up in the North Atlantic by flood basalts from fissure eruptions, mainly in the Tertiary, the latest period of violent upheavals in geological history. It is situated near the middle of a submarine ridge which came into being then, connecting the basalt areas to the east and west of the Atlantic, i. e. the East Greenland area and the basalt areas of Scotland and Ireland (ii). But that is only half of the story.

* Roman numbers in parentheses refer to maps and other drawings in the book.

Iceland's chief volcanic area of recent time, which covers about one third of the country and separates the Tertiary flood basalt areas to the east and west, is part of the fissured volcanic submarine ridge which runs from one end of the Atlantic to the other. Geological and geophysical investigations of recent years indicate that Iceland is actually falling apart along this line, even though the process is very slow. Evidence is found in numerous gaping fissures all over the median zone of the country. Some scientists believe that the whole Mid-Atlantic ridge is undergoing the same kind of a tension process, as there is a rift–the Mid-Atlantic rift–from one end of the ridge to the other. This rift was discovered some years ago by Marie Tharp and Bruce Heezen at the Lamont Observatory in Palisades, New York, attracting great attention at the time. The geological importance of Iceland arises largely from the fact that there we have the highly fissured Mid-Atlantic ridge on dry land to facilitate research. All this ridge is young and unstable. The foci of many earthquakes are found to be there, and indeed from Bouvet Island in Antarctic waters to Jan Mayen in the North it is volcanic, with frequent eruptions, both supramarine and submarine. Submarine eruptions are frequent off Ascension, the Azores, and Iceland. In recent years, eruptions on the ridge have been particularly frequent. At the end of September, 1957, a submarine eruption started on the ocean floor near the Capelinhos rocks off the volcanic island of Fayal in the Azores, creating a new island which later became adjoined to Fayal. In October, 1961, an eruption broke out in Askja, Iceland. In the same autumn the inhabitants of Tristan da Cunha had to leave their island because of great volcanic activity, and two years later there began the submarine eruption which resulted in the formation of Surtsey.

5

... hÿing af Klipperne, ...
... ...
... paa en Miile, ... ligger i N.O½ N ... .
... ... at ... ... Miiler
... ... ligger fra Eÿlandet. ...
... ...
... ... for ... Eÿlandet; ...
... ... at ... ligger ikke ... ...

Eilandet: Fortuner, fig Paaland?

P.S. Eilandet ... ... i Klippner ... paa den
... ... at det, ... vil ieg ... ...
... ... —

Aar. 1783 d. 8de Julli: Jörgen Mendelberg
Skipper ... ...

Jeg var virkelig paa de Tanker ... ieg ... ...
... ... i Bÿen; at det var ...
... ...

The volcanic belt
of Iceland

The chief volcanic area of Iceland, which has been active since the ice cap began to recede from lowland areas 15,000 years ago, lies, as mentioned above, across the country between the Tertiary plateau basalts to the east and west. In these areas, fractures and fissures have two main directions, which converge in the center of the country just to the north of Vatnajökull. To the north of Vatnajökull, where this volcanic area is about 30 miles in width, the direction of fractures and fissures is practically from due south to due north. In the south and southwest of Iceland the direction is from the southwest to northeast. Here the volcanic area is split into two belts by the so-called Hreppar Formation. The eastern belt covers an area from Kverkfjöll to the Vestmann Islands, but the western one covers the area to the southwest of Kjölur, including Thingvellir and the Reykjanes peninsula.

The volcanic areas of Iceland active in postglacial time cover about 13,500 square miles, one third of the country's area, and rank among the most volcanically active in the world. More than 150, and possibly more than 200, volcanoes have been active during the last 15,000 years, of which at least 30 have erupted during the last 1000 years. Since about 1100 A.D. eruptions have occurred every fifth year on the average. This volcanism has been

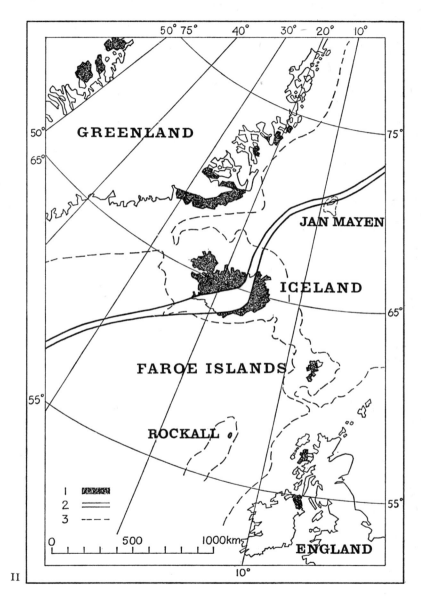

II

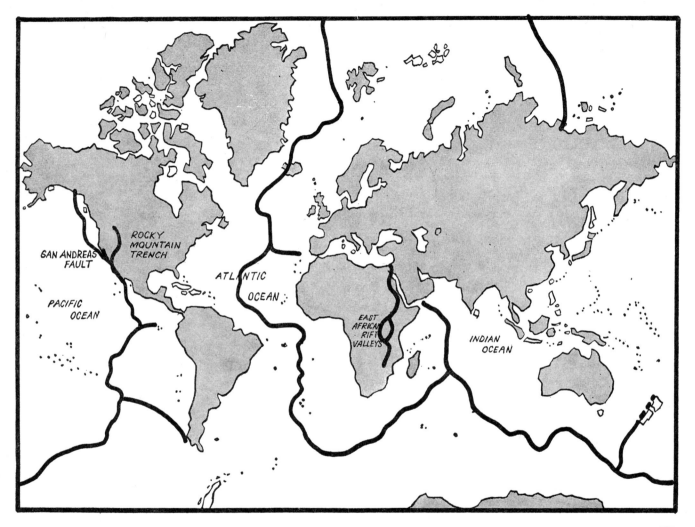

III

predominantly effusive, pouring out basalt lava from fissures and shield volcanoes, and it has been estimated that nearly one third of the lava produced on earth since 1500 A. D. is to be found in Iceland. But although the mass production of basalt and fissure volcanoes is the most striking characteristic of Icelandic volcanism it is also characterized by a great variety of volcanic phenomena. Nearly every type of volcano found on the face of our globe is represented within the neo-volcanic areas of Iceland.

As these volcanic areas are parts of the Mid-Atlantic ridge, we can expect that the volcanic activity will not confine itself within the existing coastline of the country, but may also be anticipated in the continuation of these areas to the north and southwest. This has, indeed, been found to be the case.

Volcanic eruptions off the Icelandic coasts

Norse settlement in Iceland goes back almost 11 centuries, but volcanic eruptions off the Icelandic coast may possibly have been witnessed considerably earlier. In Irish legends there are accounts of pious monks who plied the Atlantic in large skinboats (currachs). The best known accounts are those of St. Brendan of the 6th century, who finished his long and eventful life as Abbot of Clonfert, Galway. Some scholars believe that other Irish wanderers of the monastic orders, e. g. Maeldan or Bran, found their way to Iceland and even to Greenland, as the tales that have been preserved are no doubt a mixture of accounts of the travels of more than one voyager. In these tales we find descriptions which can hardly fit anything but volcanic eruptions. For instance we are told that on one of the voyages of St. Brendan and his brethren they saw a huge mountain rise from the sea to the north, its top being enveloped with fog and smoke, and when their ship drifted to its shore they saw that its summit was in flames. Later they were carried away by a favorable wind, and – to quote from the legend – "as they looked back they saw the peak of the mountain unclouded and shooting up flames into the sky which it drew back again to itself so that the mountain seemed a burning pyre."

If this is not based on old descriptions of Italian eruptions it must have its roots in experiences off Iceland or Jan Mayen. And those who had a narrow escape from the new-born island Surtsey when the volcano flung big fuming bombs far out into the sea will easily understand the reality behind the following description from one of St. Brendan's legends:

"When those days had passed they came within view of an island, which was very rugged and rocky, covered over with slag, without trees or herbage, but full of smiths' forges . . . they heard the noise of bellows blowing like thunder. . . . Soon after one of the inhabitants came forth to do some work; he was all hairy and hideous, begrimed with fire and smoke. When he saw the servants of Christ near the island he withdrew into his forge, crying aloud: 'Woe! Woe! Woe!' St. Brendan again armed himself with the sign of the Cross and said to his brethren: 'Put on more sail and ply your oars more briskly that we may get away from this island.' Hearing this the savage man . . . rushed down to the shore, bearing in his hand a pair of tongs with a burning mass of the slag of great size and intense heat, which he flung at once after the servants of Christ. . . . It passed them at a furlong's distance, and where it fell into the sea it fumed up like a heap of burning coals and a great smoke arose as if from a fiery furnace. When they had passed on about a mile beyond the spot where this burning mass had fallen, all the dwellers of the island crowded down to the shore, bearing, each one of them, a large mass of burning slag which they flung, every one in turn, after the servants of God; and then they returned to their forges, which they blew op into mighty flames, so that the whole island seemed one globe of fire and the sea on every side boiled up and foamed like a cauldron set on a fire well supplied with fuel. All the day the brethren, even when they were no longer within view of the island, heard a loud wailing from the inhabitants thereof, and a noisome stench was perceptible at a great distance. Then St. Brendan sought to animate the courage of the brethren, saying: 'Soldiers of Christ, be strong in faith unfeigned and in the armour of the Spirit, for we are now on the confines of hell.'"

The oldest extant account which, beyond any doubt, is of a submarine eruption off the coast of Iceland is to be found in the "Book of Wonders" (*Liber miraculorum*), which was written by the monk and chaplain Herbert of Clairvaux, France, in the years 1178–80. Among other things this book contains a geographical description of Iceland. The writer's chief authority was apparently Eskil, ex-Archbishop of Lund, Sweden, who was Herbert's friend and stayed in his monastery at the time. Eskil had known Icelandic clerics since he was Archbishop of Lund, because Icelandic sees belonged to his jurisdiction.

In Herbert's passages on Iceland we have the earliest known description of Mt. Hekla and a Hekla eruption, but he also has the following paragraph which can hardly refer to anything other than a submarine eruption which must have taken place before 1178:

"It should be remembered that this eternal fire is known to exist, not only under the base of the mountain, but also at the bottom of the sea, because frequently fire is seen to break with stupendous force out of the ocean high above the waves, burning fishes and all living things in the sea. It also sets fire to ships and captains, unless they flee for their very lives as soon as they can."

There is little doubt that the submarine eruptions Herbert had heard of were off the Reykjanes peninsula on the so-called Reykjanes ridge, which is a submarine ridge extending southwest from the peninsula a long way into the sea. The oldest submarine eruption that is mentioned in Icelandic sources and can be dated with certainty occurred in this area. That eruption took place in the late summer of 1211, coinciding with great earthquakes. Both were associated with the death of Bishop Páll Jónsson of Skálholt. In old annals Sörli Kolsson is reported to have discovered the new Eldeyjar that year, whereas the old ones disappeared from the spot where they had always been. The conclusion to be drawn from this is that a considerable volcanic activity took place in this area that year with new islands being formed and others sinking in the sea, but the name of the old islands, Eldeyjar (Fire Islands), indicates that there was volcanic activity in this area long before 1211.

Again there was an eruption off the Reykjanes peninsula in 1226 and probably also in 1231. There were further eruptions in 1238 and again, according to one source, in 1240. Then there was a considerable pause. Sixteenth-century annals mention volcanic activity near Eldeyjar about the middle of the 14th century, but reliable evidence of this cannot be adduced. On the other hand, we have it on good authority that there was an eruption off the Reykjanes peninsula in 1422 when an island which lasted for some time was born. In 1583 traders from Bremen report "fires burning in the ocean off the Reykjanes peninsula, not far from the islands called Eldeyjar or Gígeyjar (Crater Islands)." The name *Gígeyjar* is to be found on Bishop Gudbrandur Thorláksson's famous map of Iceland which

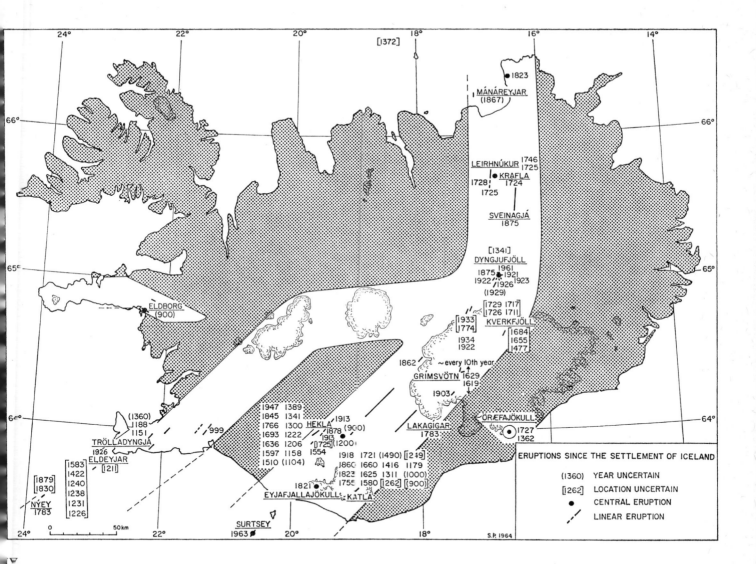

[1372]

• 1823

MÁNÁREYJAR
(1867)

LEIRHNÚKUR   1746
  1725
1728 • KRAFLA
  1724
1725

SVEINAGJÁ
1875

[1341]
DYNGJUFJÖLL
1875 • 1961
  1921
1922 1926 1923
(1929)

ELDBORG
(900)

[1729 1717
[1726 1711
[1933   KVERKFJÖLL
[1774

[1684
1934   [1655
1922   [1477

1862   ~ every 10th year
GRÍMSVÖTN 1629
1619
1903

(1360)   1947 1389
[1188   1845 1341
1151   1766 1300 HEKLA   1913
TRÖLLADYNGJÁ   1693 1222   1878 (900)
1926   1636 1206   1913   LAKAGIGAR   ÖRÆFAJÖKULL
999   1597 1158   [725](1200)   1783   ⊙ 1727
ELDEYJAR   1510 (1104)   1554   1362
[1583   [1211   1918 1721 (1490) [1249]
1422   1860 1660 1416 1179
[1879 1240   1823 1625 1311 (1000)
[1830 1238   1821   1755 1580 [1262] [900]
NÝEY 1231
1783 [1226   EYJAFJALLAJÖKULL KATLA

0   50km

SURTSEY
1963

S.P. 1964

ERUPTIONS SINCE THE SETTLEMENT OF ICELAND

(1360)   YEAR UNCERTAIN
[1262]   LOCATION UNCERTAIN
•   CENTRAL ERUPTION
- - -   LINEAR ERUPTION

was printed in 1590. On this map it is located to the southeast of Eldey. Eldeyjar and Gígeyjar are possibly synonyms, but in any case the name Gígeyjar is evidence of the one-time existence of crater-shaped islands off the Reykjanes peninsula which have now disappeared.

Now there is an interval of 200 years until the next known eruption occurs off Reykjanes, but 1783 was the year of the eruption referred to at the beginning of this survey which was first witnessed by Captain Mindelberg and his crew of the brig *Boesand* on May 1st. That day they only saw the smoke column from the eruption. On May 3rd Mindelberg saw a new island. He sailed towards it, but – to quote his report – "when we had come within half a mile of the island we had to turn away for fear that the crew might faint owing to the enormous sulphur stench."

In Mindelberg's report there is a drawing of the island (i). This eruption was no doubt an explosive eruption like that of Surtsey with the sea having easy access to the crater, since the Captain managed to commit to his sketch what is characteristic of such explosions (20).* In a report made by another Dane, Peder Pedersen, captain of the brig *Torsken,* there is a tiny sketch showing a lengthwise section of the island. No other pictures of islands that have emerged from the sea off Iceland before Surtsey are known.

The Danish Government showed great interest in this volcanic island, which received the name Nýey (New Island). A royal decree was issued to the effect that an expedition should be made to the island to hoist the Danish flag and set up a stone inscribed with the royal insignia. This stone, which was 3 ells in height, never found its way to Nýey for the simple reason that the island could not be found in the au-

tumn and has never been seen since. Its age probably never exceeded a few months at the outside. There were widely varying reports on its size, the discrepancies probably arising from a confusion between Danish miles (4.7 miles) and quarter miles or nautical miles. Its diameter seems to have been approximately two thirds of a mile in mid-June, but as it apparently consisted of tephra** alone it was short-lived.

As for the location of Nýey it may be assumed with reasonable certainty that it was situated where Eldeyjarbodi is now, i. e. about 35 miles south by southwest of the Reykjanes peninsula. In this same area, but a little farther to the east, there was another eruption in 1830. It started on March 13th, the fires being seen on and off for almost a year. Sometimes they were seen from Reykjavík. The geographical site of this volcanic activity was measured by an excellent surveyor, Björn Gunnlaugsson. No island is known to have come into being as a result of this eruption, but it had disastrous consequences for the famous wingless bird, the Great Auk *(Pinguinus impennis),* because it is believed that in this eruption and the accompanying earthquakes its only remaining nesting place in the world, Geirfuglasker, was demolished to such an extent that it had to move closer to the mainland. By then, however, natural-history museums had become so covetous of this rare bird and its eggs that in the next 15 years it became extinct altogether.

One more eruption occurred off the Reykjanes peninsula, near Geirfuglasker, in the spring of 1879. This eruption was accompanied by tephra falls, some of which were deposited on the peninsula itself. On July 26th, 1884, and during the following days the

---

* Arabic numbers in parentheses refer to photographs in the second half of this book.

** Tephra: Collective term for all clastic volcanic materials (ash, cinders, lapilli, scoriæ, pumice, bombs), which during an eruption are ejected from a crater.

guard of Reykjanes Lighthouse thought he saw an island rise from the sea to the northwest of Eldey, and the Reykjavík papers of the day make obscure references to volcanic activity. But no eruption was seen from ships in the area, so that reliable evidence of volcanic activity at that time does not exist.

The last signs of a submarine eruption on the Reykjanes ridge were observed in early June, 1926, by the crew of an Icelandic fishing vessel. On a spot somewhat northeast of Eldey the sea was "boiling" and many dead fishes were floating on its surface.

We have now mentioned all the volcanic eruptions to the southwest of Reykjanes which have definitely or probably occurred since Iceland was settled. Reliable sources refer to nine eruptions, three of which gave rise to islands, i. e., the eruptions of 1211, 1422, and 1783, though these islands have all disappeared. It is probable that three other eruptions took place in this area, and possibly even more.

Submarine eruptions have also occurred off the north coast. To quote a contemporary annal of about 1372: "... from the Fljót and from many other districts in the North of Iceland a new island was seen to have emerged to the northwest of Grímsey."

On a Dutch map of 1507 made by Johannes Ruysch, an island is indicated between Iceland and Greenland together with the following remark: "This island was ablaze in 1456 (Insula haec anno 1456 fuit totaliter combusta)." The eruption is not mentioned in any other known source, and Jan Mayen may possibly be the island referred to.

The year 1755 was one of great earthquakes and volcanic activity, and then there seem to have been eruptions to the north of Iceland, but their position may again have been Jan Mayen, although a submarine eruption is also a possibility. At the end of 1867

there was definitely an eruption off Tjörnes in the northeast, a short distance to the north of Mánáreyjar. The volcanic fires were seen on and off for one and a half months, but they were not on a large scale and there was no report of a resulting island.

In the eastern volcanic belt of South Iceland some of the most active and most productive volcanic areas in Iceland's history are to be found, e. g., Hekla, Katla, Grímsvötn, and Lakagígar, but there is no reliable evidence of a submarine eruption in a continuation of this belt since Iceland was settled. Admittedly many textbooks of volcanology mention a post-settlement eruption of Helgafell, a beautiful small cone in the Vestmann Islands, but this reference is based on a misinterpretation of the text of the Book of Settlement, and it may be asserted that Helgafell has not erupted during the last 5000 years or so, and it is possible that at least 6000 years have passed since Helgafell erupted for the second and the last time. Helgafell is the youngest of the volcanoes in the group of islands called Vestmann Islands (in Icelandic, Vestmannaeyjar), all of which came into being through volcanic activity, similar to that which is building up Surtsey now, toward the end of the last glacial (Wisconsin) and in postglacial prehistoric time, with the exception of part of the northern ridge of Heimaey, including Heimaklettur, which was possibly built up subglacially.

On Bishop Thórdur Thorláksson's map of the North Atlantic of 1669 there is an island located quite a long way to the southwest of Iceland. It is said to have been seen by Spanish sailors in 1613. We have no other knowledge of this island, and if the Spaniards actually came across an island off Iceland that year it is likely to have been on the Reykjanes submarine ridge.

There is some evidence of volcanic activity to the south of the Vestmann Islands in September of 1896, shortly after great earthquakes occurred in the south of Iceland. Many unanimous eyewitnesses on the mainland reported flashes of fire which according to their reckoning should have been a short distance to the southeast of Geirfuglasker, though this fire was never seen from the town of Vestmannaeyjar. But the time came for everyone to find out for certain that not all sources of volcanic fires of the Vestmann Islands are extinct.

Fire at sea

At 6:30 a. m. on November 14th, 1963, the fishing vessel *Ísleifur II* was approximately 4 nautical miles to the west of Geirfuglasker, the southernmost of the Vestmann Islands and the southernmost island off Iceland. The crew had just finished laying a line from the Breki just to the north of Álsey (v) southward to the point they had now reached. Then they went to the dining quarters for a cup of coffee, but at 6:55 the engineer Árni Gudmundsson went on deck and noticed a strange smell which he thought came from waste water in the wake of the vessel. He checked to see if that was the case, but not observing anything unusual he paid no more attention to it and went below to rest. Just then the skipper Gudmar Tómasson came on deck and he too noticed an offensive smell he could not identify, but later he felt sure it was sulphur smell. He also went to sleep, but was awakened at 7:30 by the cook Ólafur Vestmann. Ólafur had been on watch, and about 7:15 he felt some irregular movement of the boat, as if it were caught in a whirlpool, and it was starting to roll. He began to walk around the deck to watch for the buoy, which soon appeared, but as he passed the bridge toward the stern he saw, indistinctly in the twilight, something rise out of the sea to the southeast. Although it looked like a rock, he did not expect to see anything of that nature in this area. Then he realized that it was dark smoke and thinking that a ship might be on fire, he went down to awaken the skipper, who at first also thought it was a burning ship. He called the radio station on the Vestmann Islands to see if any S.O.S. signals had been received, but there had been none. Using his binoculars to watch the phenomenon more closely, the captain saw black eruption columns rise just above the surface of the sea and immediately suspected that this was volcanic activity. The position of the boat was then a little less than a nautical mile to the north of the eruption. There was a slight easterly wind. The skipper again called the radio station on the Vestmann Islands, announcing his view of the matter, while he had the boat sail toward the eruption columns and, to quote the final words of a letter the cook wrote to me later, "What we saw is now a matter of universal knowledge."

A submarine eruption had begun off the Vestmann Islands. When they were approximately half a nautical mile from the eruption, the turbulence in the sea increased considerably and seemed to be approaching the boat, so that they turned away for a while. The skipper believes the volcanic fissure was then being extended in the direction of northeast. The eruption now increased steadily and by 8 o'clock the tephra columns had reached a height of 200 feet and rose from the sea in two or three separate places. At 10 o'clock they sailed again in the direction of the volcanic activity, because, as the skipper later wrote to me, they felt convinced that if this phenomenon came to an end soon, no credit would be given to their account of it and therefore the captain wanted to study it more closely with his own eyes. They now got a little closer than before. The black columns ejected stones, and flashes occurred, but so far the eruption emitted no noticeable noise. The engineer then measured the temperature of the sea by the side of the boat; it was 54.5°F., about nine Fahrenheit degrees higher than normal for this time of year. The position of the volcanic activity was later found to be 63°18′22″ north latitude and 20°36.5′ west longitude, three miles to the southwest of Geirfuglasker and 14 miles to the southwest of the town of Vestmannaeyjar.

The eruption column grew steadily in height. At about 10:30 a. m., when the first aerial photographs were taken (2), its height was approximately 11,500 feet. At 11 o'clock, when the present writer arrived on the scene together with other geologists, its height had reached 12,000 feet. There were active eruptions in at least two separate places on a line running N35°E to S35°W, and we estimated the length of the eruption fissure to be 1000 to 1300 feet. At intervals of about half a minute, tephra columns rose to a height of 300 to 500 feet, and, in between, there were smaller explosions. Concentric waves could be seen to emanate from the volcanic area. Tails of floating tephra stretched out from the vents before the wind, which was northerly. Around the eruption area,

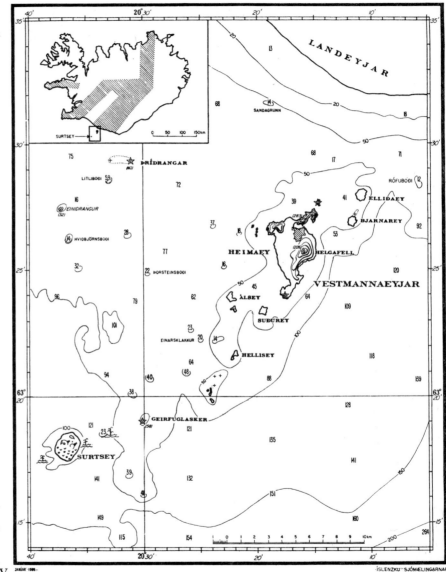

V   ÍSLENZKU · SJÓMÆLINGARNAR

the sea was of a peculiar brownish-green color that contrasted sharply with the turquoise color of the sea all around.

At 3 p.m. the eruption came through an unbroken fissure, about 1600 feet in length, with a smoke column that had reached a height of 4 miles which now could be seen from Reykjavík. The quantity of solid material seemed to be small. Outbursts of white steam banked up continually, but every now and then dark tephra columns could be discerned underneath the vapor. The sea was beginning to break on some new obstacles, a clear evidence of a ridge developing just below the surface. The following night an island was born.

Precursory symptoms

This eruption took everyone by surprise as there had been very few prior signs of such a development. At Sudurgardar on the southwest part of Heimaey and on neighboring farms, people had noticed a smell of sulphur three days before the eruption was seen to begin, mentioning it that day and the next two. The sulphur smell was also noted at Vík in Mýrdalur where it was considered that, owing to the direction the wind was blowing, this smell could not emanate from the river Fúlilækur. In the early morning of November 13th, while the trawler *Thorsteinn Thorskabítur* was engaged in oceanic research two nautical miles to the southwest of the volcanic area, it was found that the temperature of the sea suddenly rose from 44.6°F. to 49°F., but a little further east it fell just as abruptly down to 44.6°F. again.

The Reykjavík seismographs did not register any tremors which with any certainty could be associated with this eruption, although it is probable that weak tremors, recorded a week before the eruption was first noticed, originated in the eruption area. The seismo-graphs showed no tremors on November 14th. It seems probable that the eruption had a slow start, somewhat like the Paricutín eruption in Mexico, and as the depth of the sea in this area was 425 feet prior to the eruption, it probably took some days for a ridge to be piled up high enough to reach the surface. After the ridge had emerged from the sea, no rise in the temperature of the sea beyond half a mile from the island could be detected, the volcanic material being a very effective insulator. Analyses of the sea near the new island, based on samples taken during the first few days of the eruption, primarily showed increased quantities of reactive silicates. This increase is believed to result partly from sea water coming in contact with the magma in the vent, from dissolution of the eruption fallout sinking through the sea, and from material lost from the island by marine abrasion. This indicates that more of the silica content of the oceans than hitherto considered is of volcanic origin. Dissolved phosphates also increased, but to a lesser degree (U. Stefánsson in the Surtsey Research Progress Report I, p. 13).

The first few months of the eruption

In the morning of the second day of the eruption, the new island had reached a height of 33 feet and during the next few days it grew rapidly, the eruption process being more or less constant. The wind was northerly during these first days with a bright sky, so that observation from air and sea was easy. Then, and frequently later on, the eruption column nearly reached the atmospheric level called the tropopause, which in winter usually lies about 6 miles above Iceland. At this height it could be seen quite clearly from Reykjavík, towering high above the mountains in the southeast, white in the daytime and assuming a pink glow at night and in the morning (3–5). It looked quite harmless at a distance, but to the townspeople of Vestmannaeyjar it often looked threatening enough, especially when it was heavily laden with ash and cinders. At one time during the first two weeks an American airplane reported a height of nearly one mile for the eruption cloud. On November 16th the height of the island had reached 140 feet and in length it was 1800 feet. On November 19th it was 200 feet high and 2000 feet long.

The island was still an oblong ridge, split from one end to the other by a fissure which was flooded by the sea. During the first few days of the eruption there were rarely any distinctly separate vents in this fissure. Eruptions occurred in two to four places, usually at both ends and near the middle of the fissure, but the vents shifted from one part of the fissure to another. Sometimes only one vent erupted at a time, but usually more than one were active simultaneously (12) with intervals of varying length between the explosions. For example, there was an active vent at the northeastern end of the fissure during the morning of November 16th with explosions averaging every fifth second at intervals of 1-10 seconds, and simultaneously explosions of considerably greater force occurred in a vent near the middle of the fissure, three a minute on the average. While the northerly wind lasted the southern end of the fissure often got blocked by a pumice and ash wall, giving the island the shape of a prolonged horseshoe with an opening towards the northeast.

In the early morning of November 23rd the wind veered to the south and remained predominantly so until the end of January. At sunset on November 23rd there was a particularly powerful eruption at the southwestern end of the fissure (14) which closed it with a 130-foot-high mound. During the following three days, the wind blew from various directions, carrying ash, cinders, and pumice from the eruption all around, and as a result the island became a jumble of mounds and almost circular in shape. A reef blocked up the northeastern opening, starting the formation of a tephra wall. When I left the island in the afternoon of November 26th I was quite impressed by its size and prophesied that it was there to stay. But the following night there was a gale from the southeast with rough seas, and when I flew over the island the next day I was taken aback to see how much it had shrunk. From my bird's eye view I could see that the sea had cut a 300-foot-wide abrasion platform all around the island and, where the outside walls of the vent before had had a gradient of 33°, there were now precipitous cliffs. The vent had assumed the shape of a hoof, quite closed to the northeast but open to the southwest (14), and this shape remained more or less unchanged most of the time it was active. Sometimes a reef blocked the opening, but it was never long until either the eruption blew it away or it was broken down by the surf, and then the sea could sometimes be seen to pour into the vent with gigantic breakers. By the end of November 23rd the vent had reached a height of 300 feet, and on December 30th it was 415 feet high.

During the first few months the volcano showed mainly two clearly discernible types of activity. When the sea had an easy access to one or more of the vents, either by directly flooding them or by rapid seeping through the scoria walls, the activity was the typical one for submarine eruptions, well known from pictures of the Myojin and Capelinhos eruptions. After each explosion, a black tephra-laden mass rushes up, and out of it shoot numerous lumps of liquid or plastic lava, called bombs, each with a black tail of tephra. Within a few seconds these black tails turn grayish white and fume as the superheated vapor, which is the driving force of the bombs, cools and condenses.

When the explosions occurred some way down the vent the columns rose more or less vertically, sometimes reaching a height of 1600 feet. Occasionally good-sized lava bombs were hurled as high as 3300 feet. But, when the explosions occurred nearer the top of the vent where its diameter was larger, the black tails formed curves so that the eruption column looked like an enormous cock's tail (10, 20). Such a cock's tail is the most pronounced characteristic of submarine explosions. In large explosions, bombs flew as far as 4200 feet away from the island. Such explosions were often followed by grayish-white cloud avalanches which rolled over the crater rims and, after the island had grown to some appreciable height, they sometimes spread a few hundred yards out over the sea. Occasionally the explosions ejected so much sea water over the crater rims that mud streams ran all the way down to the beach. As a result, the island got covered with gray salt stripes as the water evaporated. On the whole, the explosions were silent, the steam muffling the noise, but bangs were heard when bombs crashed in the sea, sending high spouts of water up in the air. Each explosion let off a great ball of white steam which rushed up, forming cauliflower clouds, and, if the explosions were not very infrequent, these clouds formed a continuous eruption column. Sometimes the tops of the black tephra columns were hit by flashes of lightning from the clouds above.

When the eruption column was swayed by the wind, whirlwinds frequently occurred (11), rotating at great speeds, now clockwise, now anticlockwise. From the lower side of the clouds, wafts of vapor, enveloped with tephra, spun around, sucking up sea spray from below. The energy generating these whirlwinds is mainly the thermal energy of the material released by the volcano. During the first few months of the eruption, its heat generation was estimated at about 10^{18} ergs per second, equivalent to the combustion of 80,000 barrels of gasoline an hour.

Rather little tephra spread from the island in the kind of eruption described above. When the wind was strong, the volcanic material fell away from the eruption column in separate showers, each shower originating in one large explosion. Often the tephra fell in hail showers, one grain within each hailstone. The best way to take samples for analyzing was to sail a ship under such a shower, as the deck would turn grayish-black in an instant. It would then be easy to sweep up tephra from the deck or the sails covering the lifeboats. But the crews of the coastguard vessels were not very keen on this method of collecting research material, as they like to keep their vessels clean.

The eruption behaved in the above manner when the sea had an easy access to the vent. If this access was partially or wholly blocked by a tephra reef or wall the eruption behaved differently. Instead of intermittent explosions the uprush of vapor and tephra was then continuous although it was a little jerky (4), not so very different from the culmination of the eruptions of the hot spring Geysir when they were at their best. At the base of the eruption column the speed of the uprush was about 400 feet per second, whereas at a height of 4 miles it averaged 40 feet per second. The black columns of tephra frequently reached half a mile in height and occasionally were a mile high.

These more or less continuous outbursts were accompanied by a heavy rumbling noise. The tephra production from such a continuous uprush was much greater than from the intermittent explosive activity and flashes of lightning were much more frequent (7), sometimes occurring at intervals of a few seconds.

Like most geologists I am more used to working on land than at sea and I do not by any means feel particularly comfortable when the sea is rough, but few hours of my life do I treasure as much as one late afternoon near the volcano in late November, 1963. The wind was high, the waves surged about us and the sea washed the small coastguard vessel I was on from stem to stern. The volcano was most vigorously active, the eruption column rushing continuously upwards, and when darkness fell it was a pillar of fire and the entire cone was aglow with bombs which rolled down the slopes into the white surf around the island. Flashes of lightning lit up the eruption cloud and peals of thunder cracked above our heads. The din from the thunderbolts, the rumble from the eruption cloud, and the bangs resulting from bombs crashing into the sea produced a most impressive symphony. High in the sky the crescent moon rushed headlong between racing clouds. As I write this passage I realize how hopelessly beyond my powers it is to do justice to such a grandiose performance of the elements. To do so one would need the romantic genius of a Byron or a Delacroix. What I can state is that no matter how green one's face has become, the seasickness is completely forgotten in the presence of such a performance.

A continuous uprush of this kind might last for a few hours at a time. Then the activity might stop all of a sudden, and the whole island would come clearly into view again so that not even the tiniest vapor ball could be seen, whereas the eruption column was carried by the wind a long way out to sea, giving a distant onlooker the illusion that an eruption had started in a new area. When the eruption resumed its activity after such intervals, it usually consisted of intermittent explosions which gradually increased in height.

The first complete lull that was witnessed happened on November 20th, lasting for 5 minutes. On November 30th there was a lull of 15 minutes; on December 1st there was a break of 4 hours and on December 16th of 17 hours. That was by far the longest inter-eruption lull before the end of the year. Continuous uprush eruptions were not noticed before November 20th.

The first ashfall to speak of on the town of Vestmannaeyjar came in the early morning of 26th November, when all Heimaey island was covered with a layer of black ash. Subsequently, fallout occurred now and then when the wind was southwesterly. The total thickness of the deposit that fell on the town was, however, less than a third of an inch. Yet the ash caused the townspeople considerable inconvenience as they are largely dependent on drinking water collected from house roofs. This was practically the only damage done by the eruption. The fear felt by many people that fish would keep away from the rich fishing banks around the eruption area proved needless, but there may be a reason to assume that the generation of herring whose eggs were to be fertilized in the winter of 1963–64 suffered some losses, and that the effect will be reflected in reduced catches in due course.

First landings on the island

On December 6th the first landing on Surtsey took place. It was made by three French dare-devils, sponsored by the weekly *Paris Match*, who went by a speedboat from Heimaey when there was a lull in the eruption and managed to get ashore and stay there for about a quarter of an hour before resumed intensity of the eruption forced them to leave. This landing probably speeded up the process of giving the island an official name, but unofficially it had until then been referred to by various names.

At the instigation of the Icelandic government, the Place Names Committee was convened to deliberate, together with the present writer, on an official name. The outcome was *Surtsey* after the Giant *Surtur,* who according to the Völuspá had come from the South with fire and fought with the god Freyr at Ragnarök (the battle preceding the end of the world in Norse mythology). But the vent as such was to be called *Surtur* because the permanence of the island was thought to be unlikely, and if it disappeared into the sea the name Surtur could be used to refer to the submarine volcano.

Many people of the Vestmann Islands were displeased with this namegiving, maintaining that the business of giving the island a name was a private affair for the islanders and of no concern to the mainlanders. On December 13th some sturdy Vestmann Islanders went ashore on Surtsey, putting up a sign there with the name *Vesturey* ("West Island"). But Surtur reacted violently, pelting the visitors with pumice and mud so that they were lucky to escape without loss of life.

The third landing took place on December 16th, when two scientists were put ashore in a rubber dinghy from the coastguard vessel *Óðinn.* There was a lull in the eruption as before. The chief purpose in going ashore was to collect samples of both bombs and xenoliths, but quite a lot of non-volcanic stones from the old ocean floor was carried up by the explosions. We found both basalt boulders, tuff, and conglomerate with shell fragments. According to analyses carried out by Gudmundur Sigvaldason and his assistants, the chemical composition of the lava bombs and the samples of tephra they had collected before proved to be basalt

with phenocrysts of olivine (Fo about 80) and plagioclase which is 60 per cent anorthite. The bomb fragments also had small crystals of pyroxene dispersed in the groundmass. The main bulk of the material is brown, translucent sideromelan glass, refractive index 1.602.

The following table is quoted from an article by G. Sigvaldason and G. Elísson in *Bulletin volcanologique* (Naples), 1964, p. 444.

	1. Katla 1918	2. Hekla 1948	3. Askja 1961	4. Surtsey 1963
SiO_2	47.68	54.25	50.33	46.50
TiO_2	5.01	1.54	2.94	2.28
Al_2O_3	12.54	16.34	12.23	16.80
Fe_2O_3	3.44	2.24	2.37	1.65
FeO	12.34	10.05	13.89	10.80
CaO	9.58	7.09	8.95	9.45
MgO	5.25	3.39	4.99	7.62
MnO	?	0.26	0.27	0.20
P_2O_5	0.23	0.35	0.28	0.33
Na_2O	2.43	3.41	2.81	3.32
K_2O	0.88	0.95	0.68	0.57
H_2O^+	0.44	0.42	0.27	0.03
H_2O^-	0.15	0.08	0.05	0.02
	99.97	100.37	100.06	99.57

1. Tephra from the 1918 Katla eruption (Lacroix 1923).
2. Last lava to appear in the Hekla eruption 1947–48. Analyst: Jóh. Jakobsson.
3. Askja lava of November 16, 1961. Analyst: G. Sigvaldason.
4. Tephra from Surtsey, erupted on December 1, 1963. Analyst: G. Elísson.

According to Sigvaldason and Elísson the Surtsey tephra is among the most basic materials that have erupted in Iceland during this century. Its SiO_2 and CaO content is similar to that of the Katla tephra, which is also fed by a deep-seated basalt magma, whereas the eruptions of Hekla are in all probability fed by a shallower-lying, separate magma chamber.

According to the nomenclature used in the Catalogue of Active Volcanoes the Surtsey tephra is an alkali olivine basalt.

New vents

On Saturday, December 28th, a news flash from the Vestmann Islands reported a turbulence in the sea a good way to the northeast of Surtsey, suggesting the probability of a new eruption. Although the news was a little obscure and, as indicated above, unfounded news of eruptions in new places had been heard before, it was thought advisable to warn fishing vessels against this area.

Next morning a passing aircraft reported steam rising from the sea almost midway between Geirfuglasker and Surtsey, and the sea showed considerable signs of unquietness. At 1:30 p.m. the director of aviation took me on a flight over this area, where we remained for about three quarters of an hour, from 1:55 to 2:45 p.m. There was no doubt that an eruption was going on, a real submarine eruption, because there was nowhere any sign of an island, but a short way under the surface – our guess was 2 feet – three small vents (15) were active in about on 820-foot-long fissure which had a similar direction to the original Surtsey fissure, but ran parallel a little to the east of it. The distance from

Surtsey was about a mile and a half. In the case of fissure eruptions in Iceland it is not uncommon that a new fissure opens in a line extending from the one that erupted first, sometimes a little on the side, at an appreciable distance and considerably later. That was the case of the Mývatn Fires of 1725–1729 and Sveinagjá of 1875. Often it may be a debatable point whether such an eruption should be looked upon as part of the other or whether the whole should be considered more than one volcano.

It was of great interest to see the first act of the Surtsey eruption drama, which we had not witnessed, re-enacted in this way (1). When we flew very low straight above these new vents quick flashes from fire under the surface could be seen at intervals of half a second, causing abrupt concentric waves all around that made the sea look like quivering jelly. Occasionally steam columns rose above the surface, and in between there were black outbursts of tephra (15) which ejected columns of the same kind as those of Surtur, with which we had become so familiar. The highest reached a height of 160 feet. This activity seemed to be on the increase while we were there, and all the time Surtur went on at full blast. We felt almost certain that, when we made our next flight, a new island would have come into being, and in advance we gave it the name *Surtla* (the feminine equivalent of Surtur).

The Vestmann Islanders were not free from worry when they learned that the eruption was moving closer to Heimaey. A coastguard vessel went to the scene. But this eruption did not develop in the way we had anticipated. When we flew over this area at 10:30 the next morning, December 30th, its activity had slackened somewhat, and on New Year's Eve I could not help thinking that, if a new island was born there, it would never be possible to determine whether its birth occurred in 1963 or 1964. But Surtla never appeared. On January 6th no movement could be seen in the sea above this eruption area, although in the fissure area there were dots of floating pumice, showing that the eruption was not quite over. These dots were the last signs of volcanic activity in this place.

Depth measurements made in this area on February 14th showed that a precipitous ridge had risen to a height of 75 feet below the surface, and it may be assumed that by then the sea had already started its demolishing action. So much for Surtla, the island that never was born.

The eruption in January

At the end of the year, Surtur slowed down its activity, and during the first two days of 1964 there was a complete lull in the eruption and very little action occurred during the next four days. On January 7th a fairly sharp earthquake shock was felt on the Vestmann Islands, and that day the eruption resumed its previous intensity and for the rest of the month its activity remained similar to what it had been in December. On January 16th the height of Surtsey was found to be 525 feet above sea level and at the end of the month it was 570 feet to 1000 feet high from its base on the ocean floor. At that time, its maximum diameter was 4250 feet, including a wave-cut terrace just above sea level, which was 500 feet wide on the average.

Toward the end of January the eruption ceased altogether. During the next few days the island turned gray with snow for the first time and remained so for a few days, when an important new development was already in progress.

A new vent goes into operation

Just before 2 p. m. on February 1st, earthquake shocks were felt on the Vestmann Islands. At 11 p. m. scientists on board H. M. S. *Malcolm*, engaged in magnetism measurements off Surtsey, noticed fire near the shoreline on the northwestern part of the island, but earlier in the day steam had been seen to come up in this area. At midnight, glowing lava lumps were seen to fly to a height of about 150 feet. The following morning the situation was still the same, but soon after the new eruption began to gather momentum. At first it looked as if the new crater was on a radial fissure from the now extinct Surtur at a right angle to the original fissure. But during the period from the 2nd to the 7th of February two vents were active at the new site and the fissure connecting them was roughly parallel to the original Surtur fissure. The more southwesterly crater was at sea level, and in the beginning its activity was that of intermittent explosions, but soon it built up a tephra wall, blocking the sea from access to the crater, after which there were long periods of continuous uprush. This vent barred the sea from access to the one which was situated a little further up in the fissure, erupting lava fountains, one or two at a time, similar to those of the Askja eruption of 1961. These fountains sometimes reached a height of 550 feet. The eruption was probably never as impressive as it was at this time.

After February 7th only the outer vent, i. e., Surtur Junior, was active, behaving on the whole in a similar way to Surtur Senior (19–22). At times it worked with great efficiency, building up a tephra cone similar to that which Surtur Senior had constructed, and lengthening the island to the northwest at the same time as the sea broke down its eastern part. On the whole, however, the constructive forces did better than the destructive ones. In early February there was possibly explosive activity for a day or so not far northeast of Surtur Junior (at IV on the map, page 33), and on February 19th a small crater was in action on its north side (III on the map). On February 17th the island was 4600 feet long from northwest to southeast and more than a third of a square mile in area, and when the explosive activity ceased on April 4th it had reached a length of 5600 feet and the new crater cone had reached the same height as the old one.

The total quantity of tephra that came into being in over 4½ months of explosive eruption can be roughly estimated at 600 million cubic yards, which is equivalent to an average production of 50 cubic yards a second.

On February 19th an expedition was made to Surtsey with the intention of going ashore. The means of transportation was the motor vessel *Haraldur* of the Vestmann Islands, and the participants were a mixed company of scientists and eruption enthusiasts, of whom only seven went ashore, and that number would have dwindled to nil had they anticipated what awaited them.

At 3 o'clock that afternoon seven of us, including two women, stood on the sandy beach of Surtsey on the northeastern side. Some were wet to the waist, others were wet all over, and our predicament was worse than that of St. Brendan's monks, referred to above, insofar as we had no immediate means of leaving the island. Surtur was in no better mood than the bad-tempered smith of old, and now there was no Brendan to animate our courage. We had got ashore aboard two rubber dinghies, but there was considerable swell against the island so that one of our dinghies capsized on landing.

At first after we stepped ashore Surtur was quiet. Sauntering away from the beach we found a small, bubbling crater we had not known to exist right near the spot where we came ashore. We kept our fingers crossed in the hope that it would remain quiet. But we had not stayed there many minutes when Surtur began to fire warning shots, and before we really could make out what was happening we saw water spouts in the sea off the beach where we were standing. They came from bombs crashing down, which soon began to fall all around us. Under such circumstances there is only one thing for you to do, i. e., suppress the urge to take to your heels and endeavor to stand still and stare up in the air, trying not to dodge the bombs until the very moment they seem to be about to land on your head. This is really not quite as hard as it might seem at first. When the biggest bombs, almost a yard in diameter, crashed on the wet sand there was a bang that sounded rather uncanny at a close range. On landing they cupped out a hole in the sand that soon filled with water which boiled against the red-hot lava chunk.

After each large explosion and the following bomb shower, a brown pumice-laden cloud enveloped the western slope of the island so that visibility was practically reduced to zero. To those who stayed behind on board the *Haraldur* and who had to retreat away from the island because of the bomb showers, the island disappeared into the clouds. These clouds were warm and cosy, the pumice grains being so light that they did not hurt, but breathing was a little difficult due to a lack of oxygen, and a peculiar circular motion whisked the pumice grains from one side to another. Fortunately, the interval between successive large explosions was long enough for each pumice cloud to be blown away by the wind before the next bomb shower started, and in the end, after we had stayed on the island for an hour and a half, these showers relented to such an extent that we could make our way through the surf wall and row our dinghies to the *Haraldur, having* gained an experience none of us will forget. But no further attempts were made to go ashore on Surtsey while an explosive vent was still active.

Beginning of lava flow

By the end of March the Surtsey vents had been in action for almost 4½ months and had often produced material on a massive scale. The island had reached a considerable height and covered quite an extensive area, but its permanence was by no means certain. To secure long life the active vent would have to build up a tight wall against the sea to prevent it from getting into the magma inside the vent. Whether this would happen, and when, depended mostly on the wind and the weather, although in general the conditions might be expected to become more favorable for a lava flow to start as the island became larger.

In the late afternoon of April 3rd Gardar Pálsson, captain of the Icelandic coastguard aircraft SIF, reported that now the wall between the vent and the sea was wider than he had seen it before. There was then no sign of an eruption in the vent, but later that night a fire column, about 500 feet high, was seen on and off, and at noon on Saturday, April 4th, Surtur started an effusive eruption. A glowing lava lake, about 400 feet in diameter, could now be seen in the vent, from which lava now began to flow.

When I flew over the island about 3 that afternoon a narrow but swift-flowing, red-hot lava stream was running between semi-hardened lava banks toward the sea, but when it reached the sandy beach it spread out into many small rivulets which were beginning to extend an apron of lava across the surf wall. As each rivulet entered the sea a white ball of steam banked up (24). The surface of the lava was approximately 65 feet above sea level. The glowing lake spouted lava columns 160 feet up in the air and splashes flew over the old crater rims. From the lava, the sea had assumed a brownish-green color over a fairly large area. Those of us who witnessed the scene from the air could hardly contain our fascination. We had never before seen a fountain of such ravishing beauty – and now the future of the island was ensured.

Already that afternoon there were signs of a tendency which became more pronounced later. Due to the more rapid cooling of the lava in contact with water rather than with air, the lava rivulets changed course when they reached sea level, sometimes at a right angle. Therefore, the lava formed a narrow collar along the beach before it stretched into the sea to any appreciable extent (26, 35). This collar protected the cliffs from further inroads by the sea.

This lava eruption continued until April 29th. Sometimes the level of the lava lake dropped to such an extent that it disappeared altogether; at other times its level rose so that the lava welled over the rims of the vent and literally flooded the slopes of the lava dome which had been gradually built up (25, 29, 30, 37). In the biggest outbursts of the eruption one massive wave followed another, their speed next to the vent being more than 50 feet a second, i. e., more than anyone could have matched on foot, flooding the upper part of the lava dome. On April 22nd G. Pálsson measured the speed of such a wave from his plane and found that it moved nearly 1000 feet in 15 seconds, viz., 65 feet per second. This was confirmed by a motion picture. The viscosity of this lava was 10^3 to 10^4 poises. The rapidly flowing lava rivers glowed very brightly. One clear night the fires were seen from the air at a distance of nearly 200 miles.

Bluish-gray vapors of offensive smell, mainly because of their sulphur-dioxide content, rose from the lava vent, but where the lava entered the sea white balls of steam banked up and occasionally rose almost 2 miles high (25). Small whirlwinds were then observed beneath the clouds. No lightning flashes occurred in these clouds, but they were highly electrified, the initial charge concentration being in the order of a million elementary charges per cubic centimeter, and, as in the tephra-laden clouds ejected from the explosion craters, the charge was positive. American and Icelandic physicists (D. C. Blanchard, C. B. Moore, B. Vonnegut, S. Björnsson and others) who studied the electrical phenomena connected with the Surtsey eruption have drawn attention to laboratory experiments showing that when sea water falls on molten lava, positively charged clouds of sea-salt particles evolve. This may explain the positive charge of the eruption clouds on Surtsey when emitted from the vent, but it should be pointed out that the eruptive columns ejected through fresh water, such as those of subglacial eruptions in Iceland, are probably positively charged, too. At any rate, lightning flashes are as frequent in eruption columns from subglacial eruptions as they were above Surtsey.

Next to the mouths of the lava rivers the sea water was steaming hot and a lukewarm-to-hot surface layer, averaging 30 inches thick, extended hundreds of yards out where the surface of the sea was covered with a woolly, rugged vapor veil (25). This made swimming in the sea at a suitable distance from the shore very comfortable, but up to now it has not been found so pleasurable to swim in the sea off the coasts of Iceland.

The swift-flowing lava rivers rarely stretched very far. They were divided into numerous lava rivulets which branched all over the lava dome, as many as 80 glowing streams having been counted in the surf at one time (50). It was fascinating to sail along the lava front, especially after dark.

According to analyses and petrographic studies carried out at the University Research Laboratories in Reykjavík by G. Sigvaldason, S. Sigurdsson, and others, the chemical composition of the Surtsey lava is practically the same as that of the tephra. Characteristic for the lava produced in April of 1964, as well as the eruption products during the explosive phase, are sprinklings of large phenocrysts of feldspar up to 2 inches across. Professor Wenk of Basel has studied these phenocrysts and found them to be high-temperature labradorite (anorthite 66%). All over the sandy beaches of Surtsey there were on sunny days reflections from fragments of these clear greenish crystals.

Lull in the lava flow

After April 29th the lava ceased altogether to overflow the crater rims, but some lava found its way to the shore on and off during the next few days through underground channels. The continuous splashes in the lava vent and emission of gases at times indicate a magma flow to the crater, and possibly some lava found outlets on the sea floor during the months of lull in the eruption. This may have been the time when the relatively flat submarine ridge was formed, which, according to depth measurements made shortly after the lava flow resumed its activity, extends from the island to the south-by-southwest. This question cannot be determined with certainty, however, as no depth measurements were made at the time when the surface lava flow ceased. After the lava ceased to overflow the rims, the lava lake never disappeared, although its level subsided gradually during the following months. Usually the lake was very unquiet; there were breakers and splashes so that the steep inside walls of the vent became covered with semi-liquid lava which then slithered down into the lake again. The vent gradually became narrower at the same time as lava lumps built up 60-foot-high clotted walls. As the level of the lake lowered, the top of the dome began to subside along circular cracks.

The lava flow begins again

This was the pattern of the eruption until July 9th, when in the afternoon the lava resumed its flow. The moon was new at the time, but even before then the eruption had tended to undergo changes with a full or new moon. That day there was only one small lava stream which fell off the cliff above the surf wall in golden falls (28), and soon the lava flow increased until it had reached the same intensity as it had had at its previous maximum strength. The lava flow then carried away with it parts of the lava-crater walls and flooded the entire area within the old tephra-crater walls.

Gradually the lava dome increased in height. By October 15, 1964, the surface of the lava lake had a height of nearly 380 feet above sea level. The surface of the lava along the eastern wall of the tephra crater was then 335 feet, and it needed an elevation of 50 feet to overflow the old crater wall at its lowermost point and flow toward the north-by-northeastern shore of the island. This could then be expected to happen within a few months, but when the lava flow ceased in late May, 1965, the height of the lava dome was still the same as on October 15th.

During the first few days after July 9th the diameter of the lava lake was over 330 feet. On August 1st its diameter was still about 260 feet. Then there were great splashes in one or two rather clearly defined areas at a time, whereas the greater part of the surface was covered with a thin scum of solidified lava through which glowing embers could be seen all over, and the scum was studded with innumerable small spires of glowing lava. The lava was then still on the verge of overflowing the lowest parts of the crater walls, but subsequently the level of the lake somewhat lowered, and instead of overflowing the walls the lava rushed through tunnels beneath them and from there found many outlets through tubes high in the lava dome, flowing down the slopes in countless rivulets. Gradually its routes were extended along closed channels and after the middle of August, 1964, they often did not come to the surface until they had almost reached the sea shore. Some of these underground channels no doubt stretched a good way out under the sea.

The lava flow continued relentlessly during the whole of the winter of 1964–65. At the end of 1964 the activity was similar in intensity to what it had been during the previous autumn, but by then the lava vent was partially covered. Occasionally lava came to the surface at the foot of the lava slope of the crater cone, flooding the flat lava field below with beautifully glowing embers, which were delightful to watch from the Vestmann Islands. These embers were particularly impressive on February 26th. Usually, however, the lava did not come to the surface until near the sea, where it invariably split into scores of small rivulets. Often they came down off the lava cliffs in beautiful falls. Sometimes these rivulets were seen to come out of the lava cliff wall close to the sea, and on January 10th lava was seen to flow out from under precipitous cliffs on the southwest coast of the island.

These cliffs had appeared on the scene when a section of the lava had submerged below sea level a short time before. The lava rivulets were even seen to come up on the sea floor near the island. As a matter of fact, sometimes the surface lava flow was surprisingly little in comparison with the quantity of lava which seemed to leave the crater.

Although the intensity of the eruption appeared more or less constant during that winter the lava flow in general gradually decreased.

When the lava flow ceased at the end of April, 1964, Surtsey covered an area of more than half a square mile, one third of which was covered with lava. By August 25th the area covered by lava had increased to 0.37 square miles, and the whole of the island was 0.71 square miles. According to the measurements which had been made then of the socle, or base, of the island below sea level it was estimated that the total quantity of lava was then about 200 million cubic yards. On the assumption that there was no lava flow from the end of April until July 9th – but conceivably there was some submarine lava flow during that period although no certain traces of it could be seen – the lava increased by 25 cubic yards a second, but that would probably be equivalent to about 50 cubic yards of lava flow from the vent, if the volume weight of the lava when leaving the vent was not much over 1. During the first weeks of the lava flow the quantity of solid volcanic materials produced per unit of time was similar to what it had been during the explosive eruption, which, indeed, had immediately preceded the lava flow.

It has been estimated that from September until the end of 1964 the lava increased by about 7 cubic yards a second. By the end of March, 1965, the lava flow near the sea was estimated to be about 5 cubic yards a second, and on April 19th it had definitely fallen below that figure. The total amount of lava produced during the eruption is about 300 million cubic yards. The magma in the vent had subsided considerably, and on April 29th it was at least 80 feet lower than the highest level it had reached. At the same time the lava lake become more and more cramped for room, and by May 9th the vent had closed altogether, so that embers could only be seen through cracks along the scoria walls. It was the last time fire could be seen in that vent. On May 15th only four tiny lava rivulets could be seen near the sea. Two days later some lava flow could still be traced, and there was a bluish heat mist over the vent. This was the last sign of eruption on Surtsey during the spring of 1965, but other developments, referred to below, were now approaching. In July, 1965, there was still some uprush of hot vapor from the vent which could be seen in the form of a cloud over the island when the weather was still. Eleven months later, steam was still emitted from cracks in the outer walls of the lava crater, but it no longer arose from the crater floor.

Usually the lava flowed from the vent to the southwest, south, and southeast, but on April 9th glowing lava tongues were seen to flow out from under the edge of the older lava where it stretched farthest to the northeast. During the following days this lava found its way quite a distance toward the north along tephra walls on the eastern coast of the island, barring the sea from contact with these walls. But on the western side the lava flow ceased before it could protect the tephra walls from the sea in a similar way. There the sea makes ever-increasing inroads into the island, so that now there is an inlet which provides the best landing place when the wind is easterly (18). In the vicinity there used to be the highest summits of the island on the western rim of the tephra crater of Surtur Junior. It used to be a rounded hilltop, but now there is a jagged edge whose height diminishes gradually as the sea wears away the bases of the crater walls, causing frequent landslides. On August 25, 1964, its height was 567 feet; a year later it was 554 feet. Most of the sliding material is carried by the sea northward along the coast, widening continuously that part of the beach.

When the lava eruption ceased Surtsey was nearly one square mile in area, more than half of which was covered with lava. The length of the island was then 1.3 miles. For comparison it might be of interest to know that the island is almost twice as large as the Principality of Monaco and five times as large as the Vatican City. It is about half the size of Central Park in New York City.

The physical and chemical nature of the lava

As mentioned earlier, the Surtsey lava is very basic. It also proved to be very hot as it welled forth. Thorbjörn Sigurgeirsson, the physicist, often measured the temperature of the lava rivulets during the winter of 1964–65. It frequently turned out to be 2080° F., but occasionally it was even higher. The temperature of the lava in the vent itself could not be measured with any accuracy, because usually it was extremely difficult to work there. Often the physicists ran considerable risks inside the vent with lava splashes crashing down around them. Sometimes the stench in the crater made it impossible for the scientists to stay there for any length of time. G. Sigvaldason and his colleagues often sampled gases from the lava near and inside the vent, but it was very hard to obtain such samples free from contamination by the atmosphere. A sample taken on October 15, 1964, which could be looked upon as almost completely free from atmospheric contamination, consisted of the following substances: H_2O 80%, CO_2 9.2%, SO_2 5.4%, H_2 4.6%, and CO 0.7% (G. E. Sigvaldason and G. Elísson, in the Surtsey Research Progress Report, 1965, p. 39). The deuterium content of the magmatic water, measured by B. Árnason, was found to be 5–6% lower than in seawater. As the lava was very basic, hot and replete with gases, it was extremely thin-flowing (viscosity 10^3–10^4 poises), and therefore the speed of the flow was often very high. Part of the lava which was formed in April of 1964 consisted of thin sheets broken up and forming a very rough surface, but subsequent lava formation was almost exclusively of the *helluhraun* (pahoe-hoe) type, beautifully ropy.

Of particular beauty was the lava which in April, 1965, ran along the cliffs on the south coast of the island, forming a plain which was a few hundred yards in width. When I came there on May 9th the lava flow was about to cease at this point. The lava was then fresh and covered with a black, glimmering hue, and wonderfully twisted, raised lava ropes (32). I have not seen such a beautiful pahoe-hoe lava anywhere except on the slopes of Mauna Loa and in the lava pit at Kilauea Iki on Hawaii.

A month later I crossed this same lava plain again. Then it had completely lost its freshness. Sand storms had beaten off the top layer of ropy glaze, and seabreakers had inundated it, leaving boulders and sand behind. The lava plain, which used to be almost level, was now in some places set with fissured domes. Such lava domes are common in pahoe-hoe lava, good samples of which may be seen near the Keflavík road just to the west of Hvaleyrarholt.

Occasionally beehive shaped mounds of lava spatters were formed. Such driblet cones were first described by A. von Humboldt in the 1759 lava flow of Jorullo in Mexico, and he gave them the name *hornito* which in Spanish means a baker's oven. On October 15, 1964, the writer witnessed the formation of such a hornito in a small depression on the west side of the lava crater. Along this depression a lava rivulet flowed with a speed of about 1.5 feet per second underneath a thin solidified roof. Through an opening, which was about a foot wide in the beginning but soon widened to about 30 inches, lumps of very fluid lava were hurled up, and by falling down around it then gradually built up a ringwall roughly 6.5 feet in diameter at the base and sloping inwards, like the wall of an igloo. When this ringwall had reached a height of 5.5 feet only a small hole was left in the top, through which gases rushed out with a hissing sound, throwing up now and then fist size pieces of glowing lava until a bigger lava lump choked the hole. The hornito was finished, having been built up in about 15 minutes, and a new one was already in progress near by.

Later far bigger hornitos were formed. On March 20, 1965, the main part of the lava crater was covered with a solidified crust so thick that glow was hardly perceptible in its crevasses. In this lava floor there were some holes, 2 to 3 feet wide, through which burning gases were emitted at high velocity. They were so hot that they slowly widened the holes by melting the lava around them. There was no ejection of lava lumps through the holes for the time being, but when the crater was again visited the following day hornitos had been built up above three of them, the largest being about 20 feet high. From the fourth opening, situated midway up on the inner slope of the crater wall, lava had poured out, forming a small black apron on the greenish-yellow crater floor.

The lava and the sea

It was always fascinating to watch the lava crater and the glowing rivers and rivulets flowing down the slopes of the lava dome. Still more exciting, however, was the relentless struggle between the advancing lava and the sea. From the very beginning of the lava eruption it was noteworthy how much of the lava became fragmented when it came into contact with the sea. Pseudo-eruptions were frequent when the sea-surge lashed the glowing lava, causing columns of tephra to rise from the white surf, glittering with live embers after dark. Glowing lumps were sometimes hurled dozens of yards up in the air. The glowing surface of the pahoe-hoe lava tongues underwent abrupt cooling when it was lashed by the waves, forming a thin black surface shell which almost immediately broke into small black glassy fragments which were then swept down by the sea, so that the lava retained the same glowing appearance when the wave receded. Through this continual fragmentation of the surface layer, black, coarse, glassy sand was formed. The sand created in this way could be termed secondary tephra or pseudo-tephra. The volcanologist A. Rittmann calls it hyaloclastite. This fragmentation process was so rapid that slow-moving lava tongues never penetrated the surf wall, i. e., the fragmentation kept pace with the lava flow so that the growth of the lava projections was checked by their contact with the sea. In the case of swift-moving lava rivers they continued their course without a hitch under the sea down the sloping sea floor. Gas bubbles rising from such submarine flows could then be seen at some distance outside the surfwall. It was not only the surface of flowing lava which underwent fragmentation in the surf. The sea-surge often broke the lava tongues into small pieces, so that receding waves could be seen to carry with them glowing-hot lava chunks, emitting steam as they lay on the sand of the beach a number of yards outside the edge of the lava (54).

The surf also played havoc with solidified lava. Only a few days of gale were required to form precipitous cliffs of considerable height out of a slope slanting down to the seashore.

Owing to the rapid fragmentation and weathering a collar of black tephra was constantly formed outside the edge of the lava, so that at low tide one could walk without getting wet where the lava was advancing (26), if it was not too swift-flowing. The lava advanced steadily over a layer of wet tephra sand which it had formed in its course ahead. It has not been ascertained how thick this layer is, but it may be assumed that the submarine socle of Surtsey formed after the lava flow began consists of successive layers of pseudo-tephra and lava, and that lava advanced partly across the sea floor from the shore and partly in closed channels below sea level, now forming intrusive layers, now emerging on the sea floor at a varying distance from the shore.

Walking below the lava cliffs near the sea, some of which are up to 55 feet high, one can see that above the sea watermark they are principally built of thin lava layers like those of other islands in the Vestmannaeyjar archipelago, but below the sea watermark there are distinct traces of the formation of pillow lava. Some regular pillows have been observed. Occasionally, advancing lava "fingers," covered with a thin solidified lava shell, could be seen to swell at one end when coming into contact with the sea and then break off like irregular balls. It may be safely assumed that below sea level there is a considerable amount of pillow lava, both among the lava which has advanced across the sea floor and in the lava layers embedded in the sopping wet glassy sand, which, as mentioned above, is constantly created near the edge of the advancing lava. It is to be hoped that this question can be settled beyond doubt through drilling when the eruption in Surtsey itself has come to an end.

Usually, the lava advanced more or less in one direction only for many successive days, forming tongues into the sea, which fairly soon turned either way along the coast. Sometimes they advanced a long way along cliffs which had been formed before, so that precipitous cliffs can now be seen on Surtsey a considerable distance from the sea (see the map). Most strangers to the local conditions would believe that such cliffs were formed through subsidence or other movement in the earth crust, not through encroachment by the sea. But more peculiar still are the layers of sea-worn boulders in the lava, caused by massive breakers carrying such boulders a long way over the lava, which in turn were buried by new lava. Hardly anyone seeing layers of lava separated by such a layer of boulders would imagine that these lava layers originated in one and the same eruption and that their difference in age was only few weeks.

Journeys to Surtsey

During the explosive eruption there were only four landings on Surtsey, as the two Surturs were anything but hospitable. After the lava flow began there was no danger involved in going ashore when the sea was calm, so landings became quite frequent then. The first landing after the explosive activity ceased was on April 16, 1964, when some scientists, travelling on a coastguard vessel, went ashore. After that frequent boat trips were made to the island as many people wanted to see the red-hot lava vent and the issuing lava streams.

The first landing of an aircraft on the island made big news. It was a small one-engine Cessna, with three men on board, which landed on Surtsey on April 15, 1964. This was, however, not considered an example to be followed, and only boats were used for visits to Surtsey during the whole summer of 1964 until the weather began to deteriorate in the autumn.

Then helicopters from the American Naval Station at Keflavík were procured with the help of Professor Paul Bauer of the American University in Washington. They were used for Surtsey trips during the autumn and early part of the winter of 1964–65. But the sandy beach on the northern side of the island gradually got wider, particularly through acquisition of material from the western side of the island, where the sea was breaking down the tephra cliffs. Consequently landing conditions on the northern side improved considerably, and on January 18, 1965, a two-engine passenger aircraft landed on the island for the first time with 14 passengers on board. The captain of the aircraft was the best known aviator of Iceland, Björn Pálsson. His aircraft, *Lóan* ("The Golden Plover"), which had belonged to the Emperor of Iran before she found her way to these Northern shores, made numerous flights to Surtsey during the next few months, but this airfield was by no means first class, and landings could only be made if there was headwind. Indeed, some passengers showed signs of uneasiness when the plane came down to land.

In the spring a long dry and windy spell caused the beach to become so undulated and loose that further aircraft landings were considered inadvisable. Excursions to the island became more infrequent, not least because the greatest attraction, the lava eruption, was on the wane. Many were content with sailing around the island while there was still volcanic activity and were greatly impressed, but untold thousands have seen the eruption from the air. More people have seen this eruption at a close range than any other in Iceland, but the Surtsey eruption has now become the second longest eruption in Iceland since its settlement, and at the time of writing it still goes on.

The decline of the lava eruption was, however, not the only reason why excursions became more infrequent in the spring of 1965. In May Surtsey was declared a sanctuary, travel to the island restricted as much as possible to the needs of scientists, and strict rules imposed with regard to the conduct of visitors to the island. This was done on the recommendation of botanists, zoologists, and other biologists, both from Iceland and overseas, who met at an international symposium of scientists in Reykjavík in the spring of 1965 to plan international research into the development of life on Surtsey and in its vicinity over a number of years. Their project involves studies of marine and terrestrial biota on and around the island as well as concurrent studies of the neighboring islands and comparable areas on the mainland of Iceland. To make it possible for this research effort to have the desired result it is essential to ensure, as far as possible, that the birth of life on Surtsey and its development are not interfered with by man.

In the autumn of 1965 a house was erected on the island for the headquarters of the scientists at work there. Three to five men are expected to stay there during the summer of 1966 making Surtsey as densely populated per unit area as the Icelandic mainland.

The Syrtlingur episode

When lava ceased to flow to the sea from Surtsey on May 17, 1965, it was generally believed that the Surtsey eruption was coming to a close, a volcanic activity which has lasted for a year and a half. It was then the fourth longest eruption in Iceland since its settlement, and only a few days more would have made it the third longest eruption. The Mývatn eruption of 1725–29, the Hekla eruption of 1766–68 (which, however, was divided by a complete lull for more than six months and therefore might be looked upon as two eruptions), and the Eyjafjalla Glacier eruption of 1821–23 were longer. This last eruption was only a few days longer than the Surtsey eruption when its lava flow stopped.

But the Surtsey fires had not died down altogether. On May 22nd people of both Grímsnes and Ölfus on the mainland noticed a veil of vapor rising from the sea a short distance to the east by northeast of Surtsey, and as early as May 11th people at Skógar undir Eyjafjöllum claimed they saw steam rising from this same area. At 9 p.m. on May 23rd a grayish-brown patch in the sea was seen from the air. The pilot Sigurjón Einarsson estimated its location to be approximately a third of a mile east by northeast of Surtsey, near a direct line between Surtur Senior and Geirfuglasker, i. e., on the same line which revealed volcanic activity at the end of December, 1963. No steam rose from this patch and there was no unusual movement in the sea, but before 7 o'clock the following morning some fishermen saw the sea boiling in this area and brownish pumice floating on the surface. Reykjavík seismographs registered tremors in this area that day, and at 2:33 p.m. the people of the Vestmann Islands thought there was an explosion. Windows in their houses rattled suddenly, and as no seismographs showed any signs of tremors just then it is likely that a violent explosion occurred in this new volcano at that moment. Similar explosions, a little weaker, however, were traced on May 22nd, and occasionally people who had gone to the Herjólfsdalur on the Vestmann Islands, which is open towards Surtsey but dominated on both sides by high cliffs, heard the rumble of explosions from this new volcanic area.

About 10 a.m. on May 24th the brownish area to the northeast of Surtsey had grown to more than one mile in diameter, but the sea was very rough at the time. But in the afternoon of that day a crater could be detected under the surface, and was seen more clearly still from the air in the morning of May 25th, the weather being calm then. Explosions occurred then in this new crater at intervals averaging 15 seconds, and reeking lumps of tephra were seen to fly a few yards above the surface of the sea. In the early afternoon of May 26th there were fairly large explosions at intervals of 1–3 minutes with dark tephra columns rising about 60 feet up in the air, exactly as Surtla had behaved at birth at the end of December, 1963. As the sea grew calmer between the explosions the rims of a circular vent, about 500 feet in diameter, could be seen quite clearly just under the surface with steam rising from the crater rims all round. We estimated its distance from Surtsey to be about one third of a mile. A large number of gulls were hovering in the area, and every time

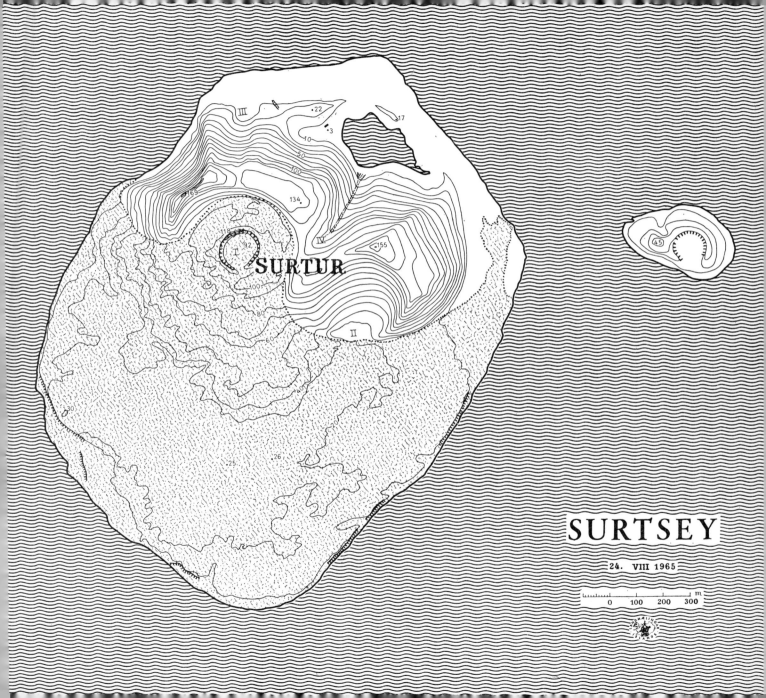

SURTUR

SURTSEY

24. VIII 1965

tephra appeared on the surface they made steep dives, evidently in the belief that this was food.

Although a new island seemed to be in the process of being born it was not until the early afternoon of May 28th that it was seen for the first time as a small mound in the sea. Sigurjón Einarsson, the pilot, who was among the first to see it, believed this mound was of lava, not tephra. There were no explosions then and no fires could be seen. The mound disappeared the following day. During the next few weeks the eruption increased steadily. On June 3rd the explosions hurled solid materials to a height of 160 feet and a column of smoke rose hundreds of yards up in the air, but fairly large patches of the sea were covered with floating pumice. It was, however, not until June 5th that an island emerged from the sea again, and in the evening of June 6th it was found to be 35 feet high and 115 feet in diameter. In the still weather of the following day its steam column reached a height of 1.5 miles. At 7 p.m. on June 8th this new island was 55 feet high and 550 feet in diameter. It had the shape of a hoof with an opening towards the southeast.

That evening I was on Surtsey in beautiful weather, enjoying the sight of the new eruption as it was reflected in the shimmering Surtsey lagoon. Sitting on the slope above the lagoon and watching the behavior of Syrtlingur ("Little Surtur") – a popular name given to this new island – I could not help smiling to myself. It was just like watching an urchin boy, with whom you are not personally familiar but whose parentage you can easily identify, because he has exactly the same antics as had characterized his father, whom you had known so well at one time. In other words, the eruption behaved in exactly the same way as the explosive activity of the Surtsey vents in their time. There were wet intermittent explosions when the sea managed to flood the vent, but later in the evening when the sea was barred from the vent for some time a paroxysm of continuous uprush lasted for a few minutes with the tephra columns reaching a height of a few hundred yards.

But the good weather was now at an end. During the following night there was an easterly gale, and when we went to have a look at this new island on the morning of June 12th it had disappeared altogether, although the eruption seemed to proceed with similar intensity. On June 14th an island had emerged again and on June 16th it had reached a height of 120 feet and a diameter of 620 feet. On June 28th it was 150 feet high and 1100 feet in diameter, although ten days earlier on June 18th it had measured 161 feet high. Therefore it probably shrank to some extent during the week before June 28th. It was, indeed, of a very loose texture, and pumice-laden patches in the sea around it were much more prominent than during the first few weeks of Surtsey's existence. The Syrtlingur tephra had found its way to the head of Faxa Bay by the beginning of July and in August it had reached the eastern part of the north coast of Iceland.

Soon Surtsey showed clear signs of having acquired a neighbor. On July 3rd the island was completely covered with a brown tephra layer from Syrtlingur. On the northeast side of the island this layer had a thickness of 8 inches. It would be hard to visualize anything bleaker than Surtsey at the time. By September 17th the thickness of the layer on the eastern half of the island had reached 11 feet, but on its westernmost point it was only 4 inches.

The eruption went on very much in the same way throughout the summer and autumn of 1965. Paroxysms of continuous uprush lasting up to an hour or even more and usually ending with a complete lull for a few minutes alternated with intermittent explosive activity. The tephra columns occasionally reached a height of 2300 feet, but they averaged about 1000 feet high. Most of the time the crater was open to the south or southeast but about the middle of September it was for a while open toward the northeast.

The island grew slowly. In periods of calm weather its height increased, but a few days of rough sea were sufficient to lower it again as its tephra walls were still more easily eroded than those of Surtsey and thus an easy prey for the breakers. On August 22nd the height of Syrtlingur was 154 feet and by September 15th it had increased to 220 feet. The length of the island was then 2050 feet and its area about 35 acres.

During the next days Syrtlingur grew still further and probably reached a height of 230 feet and a length of 2150 feet. But now the autumn winds set in and soon began to take their toll of the island. On September 23rd the rough seas had eroded away the greater part of the eastern half of the wall. During the next few weeks it was rebuilt afresh, and on October 4th the island was still 200 feet high. The force of the eruption, therefore, did not seem much on the wane as yet. But about the middle of the month there was a spell of bad weather which lasted for about a week. On October 17th Syrtlingur was seen from Heimaey for the last time. During the next few days there were winds which often reached gale force, accompanied by rain, so that Surtsey could never be seen from Heimaey. When the winds died down and it cleared up on the morning of October 24th Syrtlingur had disappeared altogether and its fires had gone out. To see nothing from the air except white breakers over a submerged rock presented an anticlimax to the good-sized tephra cone which only a few days before had erupted fire and flame.

It is not known for certain what dimensions Syrtlingur had reached above the surface of the sea before this week of rough weather started, but it may be safely assumed that about two million cubic yards of tephra were washed away in only a few days. Since then Syrtlingur has lain low.

Although the Syrtlingur eruption gave birth to a new island it could hardly be looked upon as a separate eruption. It should rather be viewed as an extension of the Surtsey eruption. The eruption took place within the same fissure area as Surtsey and the submarine ridge (Surtla), which came into being shortly after the lava vent Surtur Junior ceased its activity, and the daily issue of magma through the new fissure was similar in quantity to that of Surtur just before it died down. The chemical composition of the magma was very similar to what it had been in that of Surtsey toward the end, although olivine was more pronounced in the Syrtlingur tephra, and its SiO_2 content, probably mainly for that reason, was about 2 per cent lower. When the Surtsey eruption was drawing to its close the surface of the magma was probably close to the surface in the Syrtlingur fissure. What happened in late May, 1965, can most simply be explained by the fact that the magma, which previously had found its way out through Surtur Junior, now had an easier way to the surface at a depth of 330 feet at the bottom of the northeast side of the Surtsey cone, rather than up through Surtur, which was about 660 feet higher, with its vent narrowing or partially blocked.

One more island appears on the scene

After the antics of Syrtlingur relented there was peace and quiet around Surtsey for almost two months. Now the general opinion was that everything was over, a view shared by the geologists, too, although in answer to questions on this point I usually added that in the case of volcanic eruptions in general no prophecies could be made with any certainty. This qualification was barely adequate to save face when the news of a new eruption near Surtsey reached us on December 26th.

This time the eruption took place about half a nautical mile southwest of the island. I had no alternative but to visit Surtsey once again – I believe it was for the ninety-fourth time – and as so often before I made the trip in the company of the Icelandic director of aviation in his aircraft. The eruption was not on a large scale, and it can be best illustrated by the first colored photograph in this book, but it was a genuine eruption all the same. There was a continuous uprush of steam from an area which was about 160 feet wide and a little longer than its width, and at 2 to 3 minute intervals black tephra columns stretched a few dozen yards up in the air while dark-brown pumice floated on the sea all around. The crater rims were just under the surface of the sea.

On December 28th a small dark mound could only just be seen, a new island having thereby been born, but the eruption continued to lack any great force. Its intensity considerably increased, however, during the afternoon of January 3, 1966. Then the island was 300 feet long and 150 feet wide, but its height was only a few yards.

During the winter our "Christmas island" had a hard and difficult fight for its existence. On January 5th it was washed away for the first time. Ten days later it had reached about 100 feet height, but on the 27th it was washed away for the second time. It appeared again on February 7th, and by the 15th it was 75 feet high and 650 feet long. The following day it was washed away for the third time. On February 28th the length of the island was about 1300 feet, and in the evening the tephra column glowed up to about 1300 feet in height, with the vapor column rising to 12,000 feet. On March 3rd the island disappeared for the fourth time, but by March 18th its height was about 100 feet. Then for the fifth time it disappeared on April 7th, only to reappear a week later. Since then it has generally grown, and on June 14th, as this is being written, its height is about 120 feet and its area about 70 acres. Contrary to the Syrtlingur which was mainly a tephra cone, most of the new island is flat land and landings on its shores have involved no danger although the tephra fall is heavy at times. The activity of Iceland's "Christmas island" has been very similar to that of Syrtlingur though on a somewhat smaller scale – its production of tephra being estimated roughly at 3–4 cubic yards per second as against 4–5 for Syrtlingur.

The new eruption center is practically in a straight line extending from Surtla and Surtur Senior, running from N65°E to S65°W, and Surtur Junior and the Syrtlingur crater are near that line on either side. On the other hand the original Surtsey fissure runs in the direction N35°E–S35°W, and the fissures of Surtla and Surtur Junior had a similar direction, as did also this latest eruption fissure. The whole of the Surtsey eruption, therefore, seems to cover a fissure area about 3 miles in length, within which the individual eruption fissures are arranged *en eche-*

The development of Surtsey and Syrtlingur

1. November 15, 1963. Surtsey breaks the surface for the first time.

2. February 1964. New vent, Surtur Junior, has opened to the west of the original fissure and Surtur Senior is now dormant, a lake on its bottom.

3. April 4, 1964. Lava pours out from Surtur Junior, ensuring the permanence of Surtsey.

Legend.

- A: Sea.
- B: Fragmental lava and pillow lava.
- C: Earth's crust.
- D: Basalt magma.

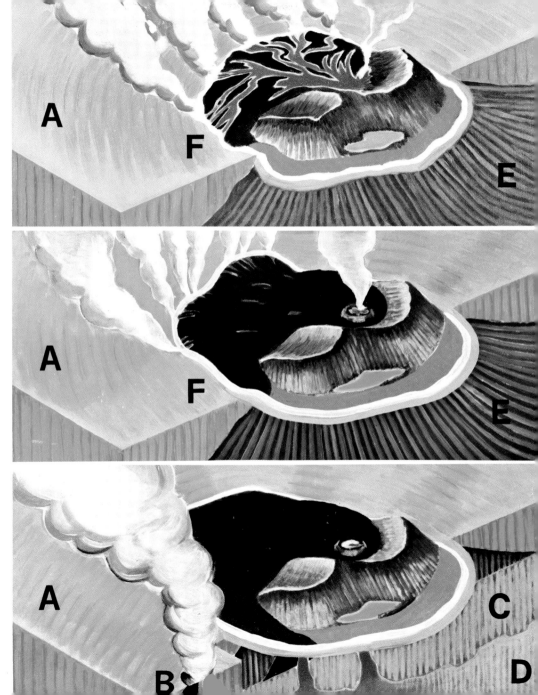

4. April 22, 1964. The lava flow at its maximum.

5. February 1965. The lava flow still continues adding to the area of Surtsey, but now runs mainly in tunnels emerging near the shore.

6. June 1965. The activity in Surtur Junior has ceased, but a vent has opened up east-northeast of Surtsey giving birth to a new island, Syrtlingur.

E: Tephra.
F: Lava.

NB. Thickness of earth's crust is greatly reduced to show magma.

The colored panels are adapted from the National Geographic Magazine.

lon, i e., they all point in the same direction, forming an angle to the main direction of the fissure area.

The building up of our latest island from the sea floor may well have started at the same time as the Syrtlingur activity finished. It can be expected to grow more uninterruptedly during the calmer spring and summer months than during the winter, provided the eruption continues, which it seems likely to do. Possibly the island will achieve a protective lava cover and thus gain permanence. But let us frankly admit that we cannot predict with certainty what is going to happen. We can state, however, that the Surtsey eruption is now the second longest since Iceland was settled about 1100 years ago. And the total amount of lava and tephra produced has now probably exceeded one cubic kilometer or 1350 million cubic yards.

Beginning of life on Surtsey

No land can be more completely devoid of life than a volcanic island that rises from the sea. Should such an island have permanence, as Surtsey will in all probability have, it would offer a unique opportunity to study from where, how, and in what order living organisms find their way to the island, and to watch their development after they have made the island their home. Icelandic as well as foreign biologists try to follow this line of study as much as possible.

The settlement of life on Surtsey might throw some light on the beginning of life in Iceland after the glacial periods which destroyed life there, partially or largely, four times in succession so that life had to start afresh each time.

We do not know when the first microbes found their way to Surtsey. Sturla Fridriksson, the biologist,

was the first to start a systematic study of the presence of life on the island on May 14, 1964, when he found considerable numbers of microbes of various kinds hovering over the island.

In the summer of 1964 both butterflies and flies were seen on the island, members of the fly family Chironomidae being particularly prominent near the lagoon on calm days. Surtsey was only two weeks old when gulls were seen to alight on it between paroxysms of the explosive eruption. "I suppose they like to warm their feet in the winter cold," somebody remarked in this regard. On April 16th there were quite a few redwings on the island. They had found a new resting place on their way to the mainland of Iceland, and various other migratory birds have rested on the island, too. Among the birds seen on Surtsey are dunlins, red-necked phalaropes, ringed plovers, oyster catchers, kittiwakes, wheatears, and snow buntings. After the winter fishing season began on the Vestmann Islands in January, 1964, one could often see on the beaches of Surtsey guillemots which had been caught in oil patches left by fishing vessels, whereupon they could neither move about in the air nor on the sea. Instead they roamed about this desolate island awaiting death (44a).

Other birds came to Surtsey with a view to settling down. There was, for instance, a pair of ravens who never left the island during the first few months of 1965. When nesting time drew near they evidently wanted to find a place for their nest, but then they gave it up as a bad job. In late June, 1965, a few pairs of kittiwakes settled on the cliffs on the southwest side of the island, so we had a bird cliff where lava had flowed to the sea only six months before. In late July about 30 pairs had settled there. The kittiwakes are not known to have built nests there that summer. We may, however, expect the kittiwakes to be the first to lay eggs on Surtsey, but so far most of the birds seen there are older than the island itself.

The seeds of various coastal plants, such as sea rocket, lyme grass, and angelica, have drifted ashore, and so have some living plants. No higher plant is known to have struck roots on the island during the summer of 1964, but on June 3rd, 1965, Sturla Fridriksson found the first green vesicular plant which had struck roots on Surtsey. It was sea rocket *(Cakile edentula),* a plant which grows on sandy sea shores in Iceland, particularly on the south coast. Botanists consider the Icelandic sea rocket to be of American origin. Its seeds were probably carried to Iceland by ocean currents, and they most likely found their way to Surtsey by sea. The plants Fridriksson found that day were very few. They were on the level ground between the Surtsey lagoon and the sea, which can be washed by the sea when rough seas and spring tide coincide.

Five days later I walked by the Surtsey lagoon, finding dozens of these plants within a small area. They were chiefly found where seaweed which had drifted ashore sheltered them from sandstorms (51). But a new danger loomed over these plucky settlers. The new Syrtlingur vent hurled up masses of coarse tephra which got sprinkled over Surtsey. The rough tephra grains wounded the skin of the leaves, turning them spotted. It seemed to me that the struggle between these little green plants and the awe-inspiring volcano gushing fire just off the shore was most uneven. Indeed, three weeks later they had all been buried by the tephra with which Syrtlingur had showered Surtsey, and there was no hope that any of them would survive. But new plants will come

in their place, and we can rest assured that the plants will win the day in the end and the island of the black giant will in due course dress in the green colors of life and vegetation.

Various types of marine biota drift to the shores of Surtsey. Often they have been pink with smaller, shrimplike euphausids (39), which have been much sought after by the oyster catcher while they are still alive. A frequent sight is multicolored cuttlefish lying on the black sand in the agony of death (44b). One of our zoologists, Dr. Finnur Gudmundsson, found on the beach a small type of cuttlefish which is new for Iceland, its usual home being the Caribbean Sea. Norway pout and lumpfish often drift ashore alive.

Seals, which are inquisitive animals, have most of the time been seen in the vicinity of Surtsey, watching developments on shore, but they are not known to have gone ashore until the tephra eruption relented. On June 7, 1964, we saw for the first time a seal ashore. In the late afternoon that day we came across the young of a harbor seal, lying on the beach on the northeastern side of the island by the side of a young professor of Icelandic studies who had gone on an excursion to the island – both sound asleep. The back of the seal showed signs of the wiles of man – it had got caught in a net – but its instinct must have registered the conviction that there was no need to fear the biped that was lying by its side now, and that professor was, indeed, a great lover of animals. But when more people came to the scene it began to worry. It stared at us with its melancholy eyes, whimpering a little, probably to attract the attention of its mother who was swimming a short way off the shore, and then it wriggled its way a little sullenly into the sea. This new island was *its* island, and an active eruption on land did not seem to cause the least bit of worry. It had found a sanctuary, which is hard to find anywhere on the Icelandic coasts while sealskins are priced as highly as they are today. When we sailed away from the island we saw that the little one had gone ashore again for a nap on the black sand of the beach.

We do not know what passed between the professor and the seal, but the former gave us to understand that by their peaceful coexistence that quiet evening a peace treaty had been sealed and signed, securing for the whole of the seal family a sanctuary on this island of fire for ever and aye, a violation of which would be a sure sign of bad luck.

You wander and wonder

When the news of a volcanic eruption in the sea off the Vestmann Islands reached the ears of Icelandic geologists in the early morning of November 14, 1963, some of them had to have it repeated to them, and received it with a grain of salt all the same. And when they in the spring and summer of 1964 wandered about the island which was being born then, they found it hard to believe that this was an island whose age was still measured in months, not years. An Icelander who has studied geology and geomorphology at foreign universities is later taught by experience in his own homeland that the time scale he had been trained to attach to geological developments is misleading when assessments are made of the forces – constructive and destructive – which have molded and are still molding the face of Iceland. What elsewhere may take thousands of years may be accomplished here in one century. All the same he is amazed whenever he comes to Surtsey, because

the same development may take a few weeks or even a few days here.

On Surtsey only a few months sufficed for a landscape to be created which was so varied and mature that it was almost beyond belief. During the summer of 1964 and the following winter we not only had a lava dome with a glowing lava lake in a summit crater and red-hot lava flows rushing down the slopes, increasing the height of the dome and transforming the configuration of the island from one day to another. Here we could also see wide sandy beaches and precipitous crags lashed by the breakers of the sea. There were gravel banks and lagoons, impressive cliffs, grayish white from the brine which oozes out of the tephra, giving them a resemblance to the white cliffs on the English Channel. There were hollows, glens, and soft undulating land. There were fractures and faultscarps, channels and screes. There were often furious gales and sandstorms, which reduced the visibility to zero, and Ægir, the Northern counterpart of Neptune, dealt blows of no less violence. You might come to a beach covered with flowing lava on its way to the sea with white balls of smoke rising high up in the air. Three weeks later you might come back to the same place and be literally confounded by what met your eye. Now, there were precipitous lava cliffs of considerable height, and below them you would see boulders worn by the surf, some of which were almost round, on an abrasion platform cut into the cliff, and further out there was a sandy beach where you could walk at low tide without getting wet. The next time you came there, glowing lava-falls rush over the sea-cliff. One day, the surf had cut a large section out of a tephra wall. The next, the lava spread across the sandy beach, protecting the cliff from further inroads by the sea (26). In this way destructive and constructive forces waged a constant battle for this island, which is and will be a true paradise for geomorphologists.

Pleasure and purpose

Most of the scientific material collected in connection with the Surtsey eruption – a volcanic activity which at the time of writing is still going strong – still awaits testing and evaluation. This eruption has, however, already taught us many things. We have seen with our own eyes how the outer Vestmann Islands and a large part of Heimaey came into being long ago. On these islands, lava sheets alternate with stratified tephra in exactly the same way as on Surtsey. But Surtsey is also an instructive parallel of the Icelandic table mountains which were built up in the glacials of the quaternary ice age, the best known example of which is Herdubreid. As Gudmundur Kjartansson and other geologists have demonstrated, the table mountains are a kind of shield volcanoes, resting on a socle of palagonite breccia and pillow lava, the shields beginning to develop when the height of the socle has exceeded the capacity of the glacier to cover it and no water has access to the volcanic vent any more. The Canadian geologist W. H. Mathews has explained the formation of similar mountains in British Columbia, locally known as *tuyas,* in the same way. A similar process has been going on on Surtsey. It may be looked upon as a lava dome on a socle which probably is similar to the socle of table mountains. No doubt pillow lava could be found there below sea level if diving of sufficient depth could be made, and, in fact, a tendency towards the formation of pillow lava can be detected at sea level. The effusive eruption which has built up the Surtsey lava dome did not start until the height of the island had exceeded the capacity of the sea to get into the vent.

Although shield volcanoes are one of the commonest types of volcanoes in Iceland we believe no Icelanders have ever before seen the formation of one, and indeed, it is by no means certain that any shield volcano has come into being during the last 3000 years. *Eldborgs* ("Fire Fortresses") of the *Eldborg á Mýrum* type, may be looked upon as the beginnings of shield volcanoes, but now it is about 1000 years since an eldborg came into existence in Iceland. The Surtsey eruption suggests the possibility that the Icelandic shield volcanoes, or at least some of them, were formed in a single eruption. It also gives an instructive proof of the fact that no clear-cut division can be drawn between linear and central eruptions. It demonstrates that external circumstances may greatly influence the formation of volcanic edifices and the behavior of eruptions and proves how steam greatly increases the explosive power of the magma. There was a great difference between the powerful explosive eruption during the winter of 1963–64 and the lava eruption which began on April 4th, 1964. Yet the chemical composition of the magma had not changed much and most likely its temperature and gas content had not either. The only factor which had changed was external conditions. At the end of March the weather allowed a wide enough reef to form in the opening of the vent to the south to bar the sea from getting into contact with the magma. If the weather had been windy at the time there is no doubt that the change from an explosive eruption to a lava eruption would have been delayed. In a way, therefore, the cause of this change was climatic. And an explosive eruption began again when a new vent opened in the sea for this same magma in May of 1965. What changed the nature of the magma was water, nothing else. Indeed, it is unlikely that so basic a magma could be so explosive as to become phreatic, unless it is in contact with water. The Surtsey eruption began as a typical linear eruption, and if the fissure had opened on dry land a row of craters would have opened with lava all round. But as the fissure opened under the sea there was first a submarine ridge, then a row of explosive vents, but soon the main vent which gave birth to Surtsey became circular. Most likely the vents of most of the Icelandic volcanoes which are now looked upon as central volcanoes (eldborgs, shield volcanoes, and cones) were originally linear.

But in addition to being instructive, this eruption has been a magnificent spectacle in all its variety, now delightful to watch in its sheer beauty, now awe-inspiring in its elemental fury. And these new islands which have emerged from the Atlantic, one of which at any rate is here to stay, also have a flavor of romance and adventure. It is just as if some of the blissful islands *(insulae fortunatae)*, which some geographers of the Middle Ages thought to be in the sea somewhere to the south of Iceland but which no one ever had an opportunity to see there, had become a reality.

The experience of a thousand years has taught the people of Iceland that volcanic eruptions are no fun. Mindful of this experience I would, however, as a geologist, apply the old well-known ditty to Surtsey:

It was both for pleasure and purpose
That God undertook to put Drangey together.

Illustrations

I. The end of Captain Mindelberg's report to the Danish Government on the submarine eruption southwest of Reykjanes in 1783. – *The Icelandic National Archives.*

II. Map showing the geological and geographical position of Iceland. 1. Tertiary basalts. 2. Mid-Atlantic rift zone. 3. 2000-foot-depth contour.

III. The Mid-Atlantic rift zone is a part of a world-wide system which is mainly oceanic.

IV. Map showing the zones of postglacially active volcanoes in Iceland and the volcanoes active since the time of settlement.

V. Map showing the location of Surtsey and the submarine activity in its vicinity (counted from NE: Surtla, Syrtlingur and "Christmas island"). Striated on the key map is neo-volcanic zone of Iceland. – *The Icelandic Hydrographic Service.*

VI. Surtsey and Syrtlingur, August 24, 1965. Contour lines with 10 meter height-intervals. White: tephra. Shaded: lava. I. Surtur Junior. II. Surtur Senior. III. and IV. Small craters active in February 1964. The Position of the highest point of the island is 20°36′56″ W and 63°18′22″ N. – *The Icelandic Survey Department.*

VII. The outlines of Surtsey at different times according to aerial photographic mapping by the Icelandic Surveying Department.

Epilogue

This book was first and foremost conceived as a picture book. Attempts were made to select the pictures with a view to giving those who turn its pages some graphic ideas of the scenes that met the eyes of those who have followed the course of the Surtsey eruption from the air, from sea or from the island itself. The majority of the pictures are in color, as there is a bigger choice of pictures in color than in black and white. Besides, pictures in black and white do not do justice to a lava eruption.

Torfi Jónsson has been responsible for the layout and the production of the book and has consulted me on the selection of pictures. But the order in which the pictures appear depends to some extent on the exigencies of printing and layout, as pictures in color and black and white have to be printed separately.

As for this commentary, it suffers to some extent from the fact that scientific data compiled during the eruption have only been assessed to some extent so far, as the eruption is still going strong at the time of writing. I have by no means fully digested many of my experiences in connection with this eventful eruption, but the number of trips I have made to the volcanic area by air or sea are now more than one hundred, and my landings on Surtsey also add up to considerable number by now. Yet I have always experienced something new on each trip, seen something I had not seen before. My description of the eruption may be found rather superficial, but I hope that it is in accordance with the actual facts. Yet, the figures I have given of the content volume of lava and tephra and their production during the different phases of the eruption are still provisional, because depth measurements around the islands and measurements of the thickness and extent of tephra on the sea floor are still lacking to a great extent.

Many scientists have done research in connection with this eruption. During the winter 1963–64 Thorleifur Einarsson, the geologist, went to the Surtsey area almost as often as I did and to him I owe much information for that period. Gudmundur Kjartansson, the geologist, also took part in some of the journeys to Surtsey, and four eyes are always better than two. I owe almost all the information concerning the petrography and the physical properties of the eruption products given in the book to Gudmundur Sigvaldason, the earth scientist, Sigurdur Steinthorsson, the petrographer, and Thorbjörn Sigurgeirsson and Sveinbjörn Björnsson, the physicists. I have received this information both personally from the scientists concerned and from the papers and reports which already have appeared in print or mimeographed versions. These works are listed in the following bibliography, indicating that American scientists have also had a hand in the Surtsey research effort, which is now financed mainly by American scientific funds.

The information about life on the island which I had not gleaned myself on my many journeys to Surtsey I chiefly received from Sturla Fridriksson and Eythór Einarsson, the botanists, and Finnur Gudmundsson, the zoologist. To all these men I owe a great debt of gratitude. I am also much indebted to a man who has committed the eruption to the graphic medium of motion pictures much better than I can do in words, i. e., Osvaldur Knudsen, with whom I have spent many an unforgettable hour on Surtsey.

Pétur Sigurdsson, Director of the Icelandic Coastguard Service, has always been more than willing to assist in the research effort, and to him and to the captains and crews of the Icelandic coastguard vessels and the coastguard aircraft I also owe a special debt of gratitude for invaluable assistance and help and manifold information about the eruption itself. Agnar Kofoed-Hansen, Director of Aviation, has been particularly helpful when I have required air transport to the island. The flights I have made with him personally or with Sigurjón Einarsson, the pilot, constitute a large number by now. I have also often flown by Björn Pálsson's aircraft, and from these three aviators I have often received information they have acquired when they have flown to the eruption area without my being in their company. The staff of the Vestmann Islands Air Control Tower, i. e., Bjarni Herjólfsson and Skarphédinn Vilmundarson, have kept a diary for me on the course of the eruption from its inception as they have an excellent view of Surtsey from the tower. Many people have sent me interesting information on the eruption and its behavior as well as photographs. It is this helpfulness and active interest of the general public which specially facilitates investigations of volcanic activities in Iceland and makes the work all the more gratifying.

In conclusion it should be acknowledged that besides government support my Surtsey investigations have been financially aided by the Icelandic Science Fund and the Bauer Scientific Trust.

The author has made use of the following papers on the Surtsey eruption:

Anderson, R. et al.: "Electricity in Volcanic Clouds." *Science.* Vol. 148, No. 3674. 28 May 1965, pp. 1179–1189.

Fridriksson, S.: Um adflutning lífvera til Surtseyjar. (The Colonization of Dryland Biota on the Island of Surtsey). *Náttúrufrædingurinn.* Vol. 35, 1965, pp. 188–210.

Sigurgeirsson, Th.: Jardedlisfrædirannóknir í sambandi vid Surtseyjargosid (Geophysical Research in Connection with the Volcanic Eruptions in Surtsey). *Náttúrufrædingurinn.* Vol. 34, 1964, pp. 83–89.

Thorarinsson, S.: "Surtsey: Island Born of Fire." *National Geographic Magazine.* Vol. 127, No. 5, May 1965, pp. 713–726.

Thorarinsson, S.: Sitt af hverju um Surtseyjargosid (Some Facts about the Surtsey Eruption). *Náttúrufrædingurinn.* Vol. 35, 1965, pp. 153–181.

Thorarinsson, S., Einarsson, Th., Sigvaldason, G.: "The Submarine Eruption off the Vestmann Islands 1963–64". *Bulletin Volcanologique.* Vol. 27, pp. 435–445. Naples, 1964.

Thorarinsson, S. and Vonnegut, B.: "Whirlwinds Produced by the Eruption of Surtsey Volcano." *Bull. of the Amer. Meteor. Soc.* Vol. 45, May 1965, pp. 713–726.

Surtsey Research Progress Report I. The Surtsey Rerearch Committee, Reykjavík, February 1965 (mimeographed).

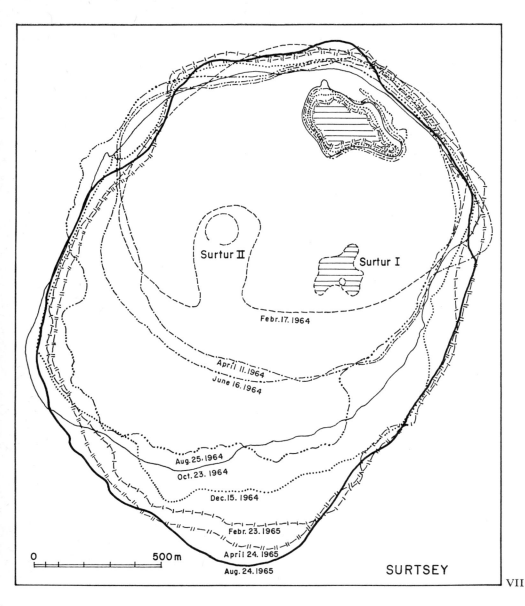

Surtur II

Surtur I

Febr. 17. 1964

April 11. 1964
June 16. 1964

Aug. 25. 1964
Oct. 23. 1964
Dec. 15. 1964
Febr. 23. 1965
April 24. 1965
Aug. 24. 1965

0   500 m

SURTSEY

VII

Addenda

Since my manuscript was sent to the printer on June 14th the following has happened.

On August 10th, 1966 "Christmas island" (now usually called *Jólnir*) ceased erupting. Its height was then 210 feet and its area about 40 acres. The tephra had gradually become more basic and the olivine content had increased to more than 30% (S. Steinthórsson, oral information). The tephra covered all of Surtsey much the same as the Syrtlingur tephra had done the previous summer, and the few plants of sea rocket which again had struck roots on the island were once more buried together with the few plants of lyme-grass that also had tried their luck.

But Surtur had new surprises in store for the scientists. On the morning of August 19th a 730-feet long fissure opened up in the floor of the older Surtur crater (II on map number VI) and started pouring out lava from three vents. As this is written two months later one lava crater is active on the fissure producing 10 to 15 cubic yards per second.

By the end of September Jólnir had been almost completely washed away.

S. Th.

Pictures

1. The visible beginning of a submarine eruption. An aerial view of the volcanic activity in the sea east by northeast of Surtsey on December 29, 1963.

2. At 10:30 a. m. on the first day of the eruption, November 14, 1963.

3. An aerial view of the Vestmann Islands from the northeast. The Surtsey eruption in the background. – Photo taken on November 15, 1963.

4. The eruption column shortly before sunset on November 16, 1963. Its height is about 5 miles. Viewed from the northeast.

5. The eruption, viewed from the mainland at 1:00 a. m. on November 16, 1963. The Vestmann Islands to the left.

6. Aircraft were constantly hovering around the eruption column like flies round a light.–Photo taken on November 16, 1963.

7. In the most violent tephra-producing paroxysms the tephra column was ablaze with lightning flashes. – Photo taken on December 1, 1963.

8. An aerial view of the eruption at 10:00 a. m. on November 16, 1963.

9. At first the island was an oblong ridge, but soon it became elliptic in shape, split from one end to the other. – Photo taken on November 16, 1963.

10. "Cock's tail" explosions like the one on the right were characteristic of the eruption while the sea had an easy access to the lava lake in the vent. At the end of each tephra "plume" there is a bomb. – Photo taken on November 19, 1963.

11. A vortex descends from the eruption column as it is carried by the wind, whirling pumice about and lashing the sea. – Photo taken on November 15, 1963.

12. A view of the island from the northwest on November 19, 1963. Its maximum height is now 195 feet and its length is 2000 feet.

13. A close-up taken from the air on November 16, 1963.

14. A violent continuous uprush in the southwesternmost crater on November 23rd at 3 p. m. The crater wall to the right is 330 feet high.

15. Three small submarine vents are active in a 820-foot-long fissure about 1.6 miles east by northeast of Surtsey. – Photo taken at 2 p. m. on December 29, 1963.

16. Surtsey, viewed from the air on November 30, 1963. The vent is open to the southwest. The island is now 2600 feet in diameter.

17. Surtur changes into his winter outfit after his long spell of intensive action has come to an end. Its height is now 671 feet. On its northwestern side Surtur Junior is in action. – Photo taken on February 4, 1964.

18. Scientists going ashore under tephra cliffs on the west side of Surtsey on August 1, 1964.

19. An explosion of Surtur on March 1, 1964.

20. A typical "cock's tail" explosion. Its height is 1300 feet. – Photo taken on February 19, 1964.

21. Surtur Junior exploding intermittently on February 19, 1964.

22. Surtur Junior exploding intermittently on March 1, 1964.

23. The Surtsey eruption on February 5, 1964, viewed from the southeast. In the western end of the fissure a continuous uprush is at its height, piling up a scoria wall which bars the sea from flowing into the eastern part of the fissure where lava fountains are playing.

24. Effusive activity began on Surtsey at noon on April 4, ensuring a long life for the island.

25. Lava flow at its height. – Photo taken on April 20, 1964.

26. Lava flowing southeast over the abrasion platform of Surtsey, protecting the sea-cliff from further encroachments by the sea. – Photo taken on April 11, 1964.

27. Lava versus the sea. – Photo taken on the southeast coast of Surtsey on February 28, 1965.

28. After 10 weeks of turbulent activity in the lava vent without overflowing, the lava resumed its flow to the sea on July 9, 1964, when this picture was taken. Tindafjallajökull, Eyjafjallajökull, and the Vestmann Islands in the background.

29. Lava overflowing the crater rim at a speed of 60 feet a second. – Photo taken on April 22, 1964.

30. The mouth of a lava stream at night. – Photo taken on April 20, 1964.

31. Water channels on the northeastern slope of Surtsey. – Photo taken on February 20, 1965.

32. Fresh pahoe-hoe lava under sea cliffs on the southernmost part of Surtsey. – Photo taken on May 9, 1965.

33. The lava vent on May 21, 1964.

34. Sea-cliff on the southeastern side of Surtsey. Geirfuglasker, Geldingur and Súlnasker in background. – Photo taken on April 16, 1964.

35. An aerial photograph of Surtsey, taken on June 16, 1964.

36. Surtsey lagoon formed in late February, 1964, mainly because of subsidence. Its depth is 10 to 13 feet. – Photo taken on April 16, 1964.

37. Lava streams rush down the dome towards the sea, one branch flooding the depression between the crater cone and the old crater rim and flowing back into the vent through an opening in the wall. – Photo taken on April 20, 1964.

38. Fire and sea. – Photo taken on April 17, 1964.

39. Euphausids below high tide level in the sand of the beach on the northwestern side of Surtsey.– Photo taken on April 16, 1964.

40a. and b. Gulls have by this time taken to Surtsey, and a young seal has sought refuge there. – Photos taken on June 7, and August 1, 1964.

41. The lava vent on August 17, 1964. Height of lava fountain about 250 feet.

42. Pahoe-hoe lava. – Photo taken on February 20, 1965.

43. A view through an opening in the roof of a lava tunnel. – Photo taken on August 17, 1964.

44a. A guillemot, which has been caught in a patch af oil, awaiting death on the northern coast of Surtsey. – Photo taken on February 20, 1965.

44b. Cuttlefish on the sandy beach of Surtsey. – Photo taken on January 31, 1965.

45. Pahoe-hoe lava overflowing solidified lava with precipitations. – Photo taken on March 19, 1965.

46–47. Precipitations on the Surtsey lava. – Photos taken on March 14, 1965.

48. Lava formation. – Photo taken on March 14, 1965.

49. Three lava rivulets. Eyjafjallajökull in the background. – Photo taken on March 14, 1965.

50. A view of the lava edge meeting the sea. – Photo taken on February 6, 1965.

51. The first plant. Sea Rocket (*Cakile edentula*) on the northern shore of the Surtsey lagoon. – Photo taken on June 8, 1965.

52. Surtsey and Syrtlingur. An aerial view from the north on June 8, 1965.

53. Aerial view of Syrtlingur on June 24, 1965.

54. Lava falling off cliffs on the south side of Surtsey. Steam rises from pieces of lava carried out from an alvancing lava tongue by a receding wave. – Photo taken on February 20. 1065.

Picture credits

Hjálmar Bárdarson 8, 33, 36

Sigurjón Einarsson 1, 3

Sverrir Einarsson 20

Jón E. Gudjónsson 5

Rafn Hafnfjörd 45, 46, 47

Kristinn Helgason 3, 13

Icelandic Surveying Department 35

Albert Jónasson 30

Sigurgeir Jónasson 7, 19, 21, 22

Ævar Jóhannesson 38, 42, 43, 48, 54

Ingimundur Magnússon 2

Kristján Magnússon 10, 12

Gardar Pálsson 25, 29

Sigurdur Thorarinsson 4, 6, 11, 14, 15, 16, 17, 23, 24, 26, 27, 28, 31, 32, 34, 37, 39, 40a, 44, 49, 50, 51, 52, 53

Jón Thórdarson 41

Thórhallur Vilmundarson 18, 40b

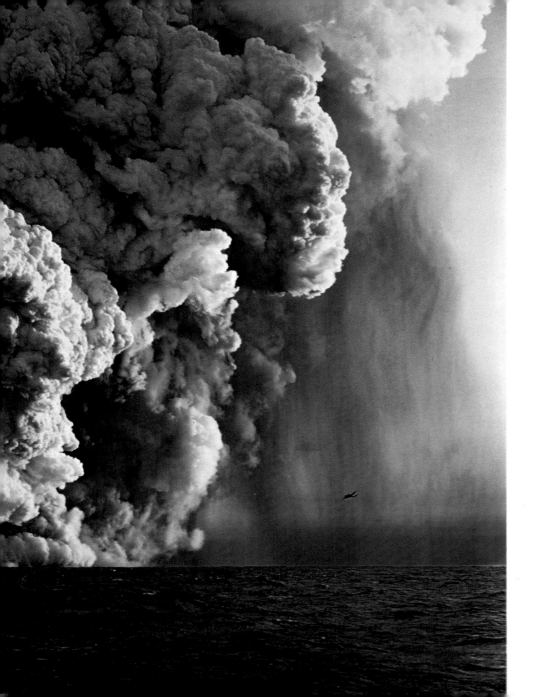

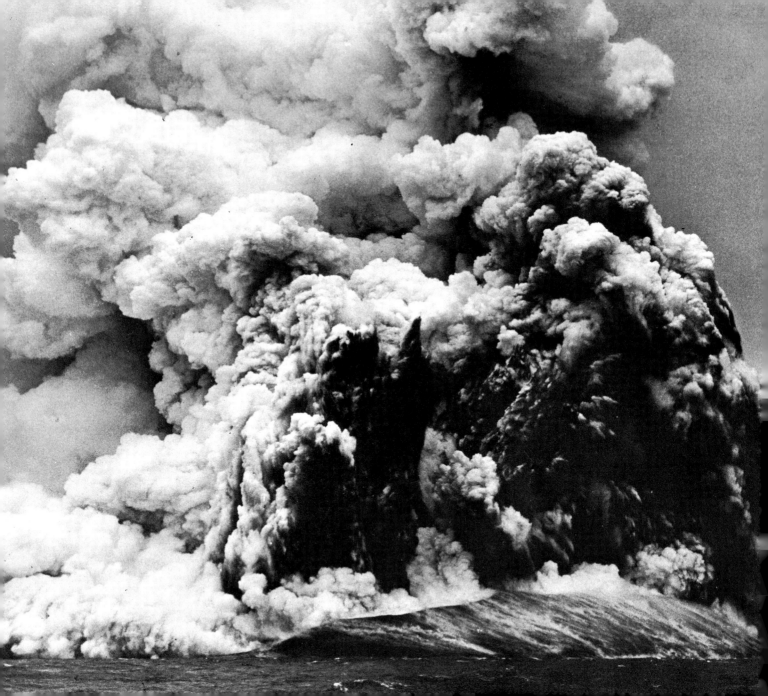

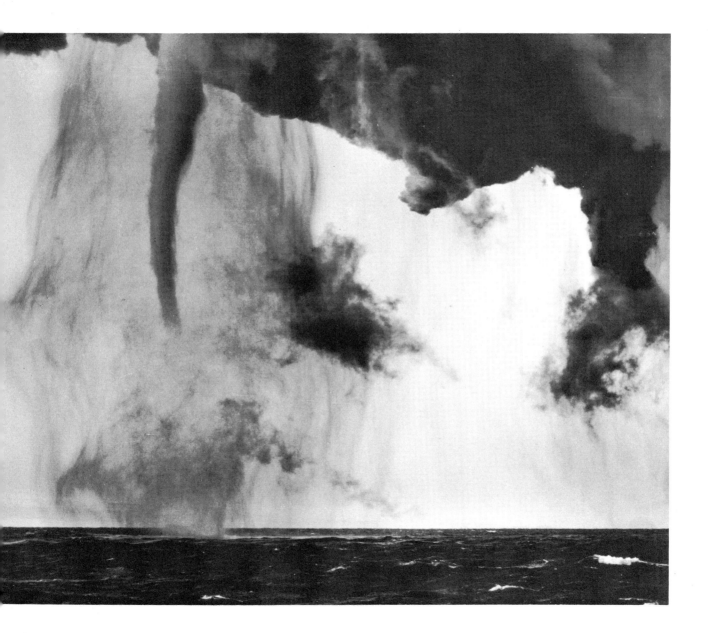

15

23-24

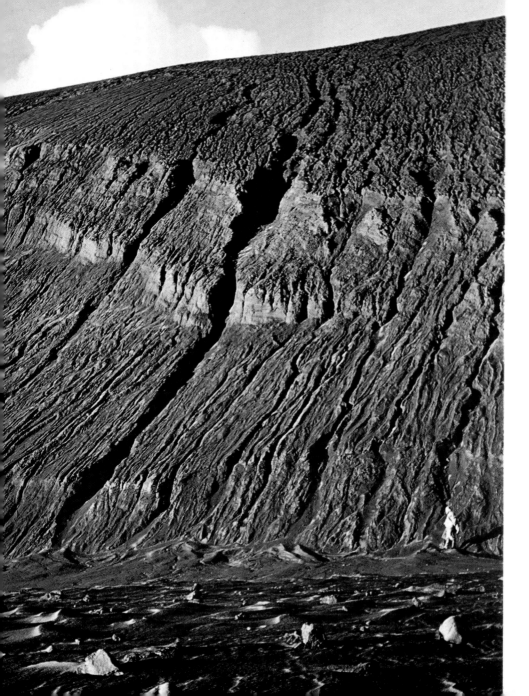

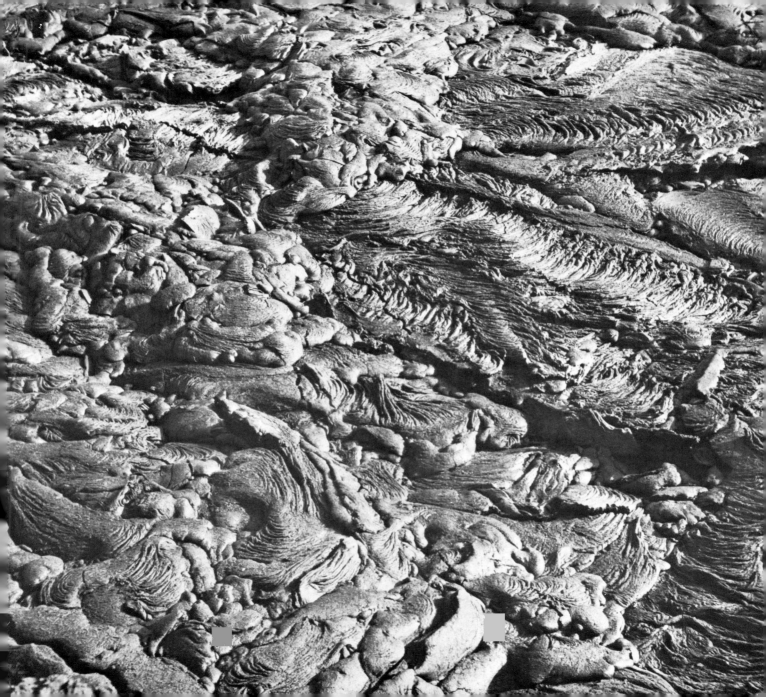

33

37

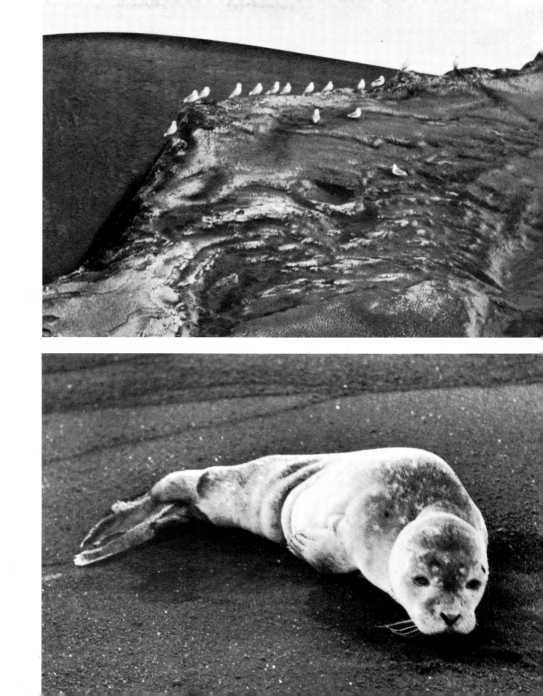

51

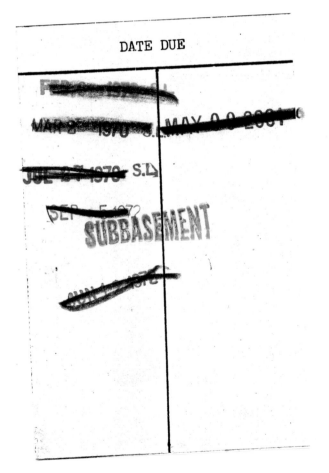